Hellebores

Hellebores

Christmas Rose, Lenten Rose

Marlene Sophie Ahlburg

Translated by Marlene Sophie Ahlburg and
Jennifer Hewitt

B.T. Batsford Ltd · London

This edition first published 1993
Translation © Marlene Sophie
Ahlburg and Jennifer Hewitt 1993
German edition © 1989 by Eugen Ulmer
GmbH & Co., Stuttgart, Germany

Typeset by J&L Composition Ltd, Filey,
North Yorkshire

and printed in Great Britain by
Bookcraft, Midsomer Norton

Published by
B.T. Batsford Ltd
4 Fitzhardinge Street
London W1H 0AH

A catalogue record for this book is
available from the British Library

ISBN 0 7134 7058 5

CONTENTS

Acknowledgements 6
Foreword 7

Evolution and Dispersion 8
The Development of the Genus
Helleborus 8
 Distribution of the Genus
 Helleborus in the Northern
 Hemisphere 12

Morphology 15
 The Seedling 15
 The Adult Plant 19
  Underground Parts 19
  The Leafy Part 19
  The Inflorescence of the
  Caulescentes 22
  The Inflorescence of Species
  with Radical Leaves 26
  The True Leaves 26
  The Sheaths 28
  The Bracts 29
  The Flower 32
  The Fruit 34
  The Seeds 35

Descriptions of the Species 36
 Species with Rhizomes and
 Radical Leaves 36
  Helleborus thibetanus 36
  Helleborus orientalis 37
  Helleborus cyclophyllus 41
  Helleborus odorus 42
  Helleborus multifidus 43
  Helleborus torquatus 48
  Helleborus purpurascens 49
  Helleborus dumetorum 50
  Helleborus atrorubens 51

  Helleborus viridis 52
  Helleborus niger 54
 Species with a Surface Stem 58
  Helleborus lividus 58
  Helleborus argutifolius 62
  Helleborus foetidus 64
  Helleborus vesicarius 67
**Origin of Garden Forms and
Hybridization** 69
 Natural Hybrids and Selected
 Forms 69
  'Intermedius' 69
  'Torquatus' 72
 Hybrids of Garden Origin 73
  Helleborus × nigercors 76
  A Hybrid raised by Helen
  Ballard 77
  Helleborus × sternii 78
  'Wintersilber' 79
  'Atrorubens' 80
 Work on the Genus up to the
 Present Day 83
 Thoughts on Hybridizing 88
Cultivation and Use 92
 Propagation by Seed and
 Division 93
 Planting and General Care 98
 Hellebores in Winter 101
 Pests and Diseases 105
 Use in the Garden 107
 Use in Flower Arranging and
 Floristry 115
 Helleborus in Medicine 118
Appendices 120
 Bibliography 120
 Hellebore Nurseries 121
Glossary of Botanical Terms 122
Index 125

ACKNOWLEDGEMENTS

Photographs

Ahlburg, G., Rötgesbüttel: Plate 3 top right, middle right, Plate 4 bottom right, Plate 5 bottom right, Plate 6 all, Plate 7 top right, middle left and right, bottom left and right, Plate 8 bottom left and right.

Lehmann, J., Kippenheim: Plate 1 top left.

Reinhard, H., Heiligkreuzsteinach: Plate 4 top right.

Reiser, E., Wetzlar: Plate 1 top right and bottom, Plate 2 top right, middle left, bottom left and right, Plate 3 top left, middle left, bottom left, Plate 4 bottom left, Plate 7 top left.

Schacht, W., Frasdorf: Plate 3 bottom right, Plate 4 top left, middle right.

Seidl, S., München: jacket photograph, Plate 2 top left, Plate 5 top left, bottom left.

Strauss, F., Thalhausen: Plate 8 top.

Drawings

All drawings (with the exception of the two diagrams pages 16 and 66 from *Monographia Hellebororum* by V. Schiffner 1891) by Bettina Jahn, from sketches provided by the author, and partly from other literature.

FOREWORD

The last true scientific monograph on the genus *Helleborus* was written by Ernst Ulbrich in 1938. With the exception of only two changes, it corresponds with *Monographia Hellebororum* that Viktor Schiffner wrote in 1898. Further work has been done on *Helleborus* in comprehensive works of systematic botany, including Brian Mathew's *Hellebores* in 1989, which is mainly a scientific work but also contains a good deal of advice on cultivation. However, apart from a little booklet by Brian Mathew there has been nothing that could be regarded as a book for gardeners.

I have been intending to write a book on *Helleborus* for years, but something has always been lacking – the time, the garden, the plants, the detailed knowledge. But when, at last, all these things came together, the book almost wrote itself, and it was not hard work but a relaxing, enjoyable hobby.

Many kind people have helped me with advice and material. I should particularly like to mention Jennifer Hewitt, who supplied me with literature for comparison, and who has always taken a keen interest. Hermann Fuchs provided valuable plant material obtained from the wild and made great efforts to help me with vital observations. I also wish to thank Wilhelm Schacht, Erich Pasche, Helen Ballard, Heinz Klose, Dr Tura Ekim of Ankara, Dr Türker Altan of Adana, and Brian Mathew for their help. And I would not like to forget to mention that valuable plants were sent to me from the Royal Botanic Gardens, Kew; the Royal Horticultural Society's Garden, Wisley; and the Savill Gardens.

Bettina Jahn's drawings have added to the accurate botanical information, and my husband, Georg Ahlburg, and other photographers helped me by providing colour photographs that show all the beauty of these flowers.

Of course it would be impossible to publish a manuscript without a publisher who approves the subject, produces the book, and gives it every support. So I thank Roland Ulmer, Dr Volk, and Timothy Auger, who have given me the chance to offer the results of my enthusiasm to other people. I hope that it may win the genus *Helleborus* many new friends.

Rötgesbüttel
Marlene Sophie Ahlburg

EVOLUTION AND DISPERSION

The Development of the Genus *Helleborus*

The genus *Helleborus* belongs to the flowering plants, to the family Ranunculaceae. The first flowering plants are thought to have originated during the Jurassic period, in south-east Asia. Perhaps the ancestors of *Helleborus* spread along the shores of the Tethys to the West. During the folding of the Earth's crust that thrust up the mountains from the Himalaya to the Pyrenees they may have spread into the subtropical zone, which at times reached as far north as southern England and southern Scandinavia, though later in their travels the climate became less kind. After that they were forced – at least in glaciated areas – to recede to small ice-free islands in valleys at the foot of mountain chains. In interglacial periods they could spread again. This occurred at least three times – small movements of the icecap can be ignored – and it took about 1½ million years. Glacial and interglacial periods changed the genetic make-up of living organisms as useful mutations became firmly fixed and gradually the appearance of the plants was altered or their physiological functions changed.

After the so-called Ice Age, the climate did not revert to being as warm as it was before the development of the great folded mountain ranges, so adaptations which had evolved were still useful. Because a glacial period was always followed by an interglacial, these adaptations were for cold climates, as well as for warm. They resulted not so much in absolute hardiness and heat resistance, but in the capacity to postpone or defer the growing and flowering seasons, even to interrupt them. *Helleborus* could live and multiply in conditions ranging from the winter rains of Asia Minor, alternating frost (with and without snow cover) and thaw in north-western Europe, dry summers in the hills around the Mediterranean, and wet summers in temperate hilly regions, to subalpine climates.

When the climatic zones moved south, *Helleborus* did not die out in the areas they had colonized. In addition to their capacity to change or interrupt their growth, all hellebore species developed a greater or lesser ability to react to frost by reducing the water content of their cells. When the temperature rises, it returns to normal again. They can probably even alter the freezing point of their tissues. This can be seen when the flower stems, which droop or even lie flat on the ground after a frosty night, become completely erect again as the temperature rises. It is not known whether *Helleborus thibetanus* can do this, as up-to-date information has not been available from China, and seeds have only recently been sent to Britain.

In addition to the characteristics already mentioned, some European species are greatly helped by their leaves dying off in winter. Quite the opposite of this are the evergreen, stem-producing species (plus *H. niger*) with smooth leathery leaves that are particularly well adapted to the warmth and drought of the Mediterranean region. While *H. vesicarius* reacts to the hot, dry conditions of its native habitat by retreating underground from the end of spring until the winter rains awaken it again. The rest of the species live somewhere between these two extremes and have a thick skin that protects them from all kinds of inclement weather.

Ulbrich states that *Helleborus thibetanus* is the only member of the genus that can be called a thin-leaved, soft plant. It has red or white flowers and grows in the rainforests of China in moist and mossy ground. Whether or not it is deciduous is unknown. One can imagine that this might be the type of plant whose descendants advanced by seeding, generation after generation, from the East to the West. During the long journey through zones and time they

were exposed to all kinds of stress and disease, so most of the developing forms were not long-lived. The next descendent still in existence, *H. vesicarius*, developed into a very different species owing to its geographic and climatic isolation in south-east Turkey and northern Syria.

At the Bosphorus the areas of the Asiatic and European species meet, so the Balkan species *Helleborus cyclophyllus* and *H. odorus* seem to be undecided as to their exact form. They show this through certain morphologic features. In most years *Helleborus cyclophyllus* is deciduous, and the seed capsules on most plants are similar to those of *H. orientalis* in that each capsule is held on its own very short 'stem'. But there are places where colonies of *H. cyclophyllus* can be found in which the capsules are united at the base with neighbouring capsules, or at least with the cone-shaped receptacle as in the rest of the European species. This means that these plants are on the way to developing a true closed ovary, which gives the seeds much better protection against weather damage. Something similar is seen in *H. odorus*. Like *H. cyclophyllus* it is sometimes deciduous but not generally so, and it seems that this species is not certain whether such behaviour is useful. Its capsules are always fused at their bases. Both species seem to be still slightly Asiatic and not wholly European if one looks at their adaptation to climate and the evolution of their reproductive organs.

Many European species lose their

leaves at the onset of or during winter. Their flowers emerge from the ground in spring among dry, withered, grey-brown leaves. All have seed capsules that are fused together at the bases but free above that, so these species, too, have not yet reached the goal of this development, the true, closed ovary. Nor has *Helleborus vesicarius*.

In spite of being morphologically different from the stemmed species and belonging to the Acaulescentes with radical leaves, *Helleborus niger* is obviously closer to the Caulescentes as it sometimes hybridizes with *H. argutifolius* and *H. lividus*; the type of bracts it has also brings it close to *H. argutifolius* and *H. foetidus*, but it does not hybridize with the latter species.

Helleborus foetidus has evolved further than its relatives, as this most westerly species has the most effective form of reproduction. It does not hybridize with any other members of the genus, though a forced cross with *H. argutifolius* has been made in a laboratory.

Most species, with the exception of *Helleborus niger* and *H. cyclophyllus*, have pendant flowers and thus protect their reproductive organs very effectively; only one form of *H. orientalis* from near Ankara has sideways-facing flowers, and some straighten their pedicels after pollination by contraction of a sort of crêpe-skin beneath the flower. Some flowers of *H. cyclophyllus* also do this. All the species produce nectar in the nectaries. These were originally petals, which gradually changed into nectaries. And nearly all the species have colourful petals that help to attract insects.

Helleborus niger in the northern Alps normally has only one or two flowers to a stem, but the southern subspecies *H. n. macranthus* has two or three, like *H. viridis* and *H. purpurascens* which have three to five flowers per stem. All the other species have five to twelve, particularly in favourable conditions, and some even up to sixteen, with very pretty, big, bowl- or bell-shaped flowers in some species. These multi-flowered stems are another development that helps to increase pollination by insects, a trend intensified among the stemmed species, particularly *H. foetidus*.

All hellebores have flowers that are saucer- or bowl-shaped, or which become bell-shaped. In this case *Helleborus foetidus* is the odd one out, as the mouth of the flower is so contracted as to have become almost a bell.

In addition to all the above, the plurality of some flower parts and the variability of their numbers, and the existence of transitional elements (for instance, between bracts and tepals) show that this is a very early group of plants.

As well as the flower colours that have evolved, some European species have a delicate fragrance. *Helleborus odorus* and *H. dumetorum* smell of blackcurrants to some people, and of elderberry to others. The young flowers of *H. lividus* produce a sweet scent similar to *Viola odorata* or wallflower, but it is only perceptible when the plant is grown under cover. *H. cyclophyllus* sometimes smells of honey. Some clones of *H. multifidus*, and even *H. foetidus*, can smell very pleasant.

Another safeguard in the preservation of a species can be seen in *H. foetidus*, whose flowers open in succession; in mild winters this can continue from December to the end of April.

Because the hellebore flower is not highly specialized, it can be pollinated by a variety of insects. If looked at from the side it seems as if the filaments and anthers form a passage for beetles. In some species they are so densely packed that small solitary bees can walk about on them collecting pollen. However, the nectar is so deeply hidden in the cornet-shaped nectaries that only insects with a long proboscis, like bees and bumblebees, can collect it.

All members of the genus are protogynous, so cross-fertilization is the normal method of pollination. Despite this, the genus is generally self-fertile, a useful character for both arctic and hot, dry climatic conditions.

Looking at all this, and weighing one fact against another, one cannot but get the impression that here we have a genus that does not intend to miss any chance of reaching its goal, or that it is still in the process of evolution and exploring every possibility which may be useful to the plants.

When we separate *Helleborus niger* and the stem-producing species from the rest and look at the two large groups of species with radical leaves (with no clear demarcation lines between different species and all of them able to hybridize with one another) we are inclined to ask whether the flexibility of the genus is not, in fact, a progression; perhaps we have a finger on the pulse of evolution?

Helleborus foetidus and *H. vesicarius* are found at the extremes of the area inhabited by the genus. Each has responded to this in its own way and, by developing more highly or by intense specialization, isolated itself from the rest of the group. But *H. niger*, which took a separate path and moved northwards and high into the mountains, formed its morphology by discarding every character not absolutely essential, so that it could almost be called a simplified plant.

Distribution of the Genus *Helleborus* in the Northern Hemisphere

The genus is restricted to the northern hemisphere and occurs only in Europe and Asia. In North America *Helleborus orientalis* is represented mainly by its hybrids as a garden plant. Species formerly used in medicine may still grow in some places where they have become naturalized, having been brought into the country by immigrants.

Those interested in the subject can find a long list of places where the different species used to grow in the *Monographia Hellebororum* by Viktor Schiffner. However, this was written in 1891 and things have probably changed since then. In 1938 Ernst Ulbrich drew a distribution map for the species, but excluded *Helleborus thibetanus* which occurs in China. All the forms he considered to be separate species are shown on this map. Today some of them are grouped together, and *H. cyclophyllus* is now found only in Greece. An updated map was published by Brian Mathew in *Hellebores* in 1989.

All the Turkish forms are now grouped under the species name *Helleborus orientalis* Lam., with the exception of *Helleborus vesicarius* Auch.-Elroy. *H. vesicarius* is found only in the region around Adana, partly in southern Turkey and partly in northern Syria, which is extremely dry in summer. *H. cyclophyllus* Boiss. is native to Greece. It is the only hellebore to be found there, so is naturally called the Greek Hellebore.

Helleborus odorus Waldst. et Kit. is very similar to *H. cyclophyllus*. It is widely distributed in southeast Europe and is therefore very variable. The centre of its area is in Yugoslavia and it is also found in Hungary, Bulgaria, Romania and northern Italy. Reports of its occurrence in Albania have not been confirmed. The species native to Albania is *H. multifidus* Visiani, which in its many variations is also spread all over Yugoslavia.

Brian Mathew has recently given species status to the reddish-flowered *H. multifidus* subsp. *serbicus*, calling it *H. torquatus* Archer-Hind. *H. dumetorum* Waldst. et Kit. grows in the same areas as *H. odorus* and *H. multifidus*, as do two still rarer forms that play a part in the literature, namely 'Torquatus' and 'Intermedius'. It is also possible to find *H. purpurascens* Waldst. et Kit. in a few places, but mainly in Hungary. Older plants of *H. purpurascens* show some similarity to *H. multifidus* and, more obviously, to 'Torquatus' and 'Intermedius' (both of which are included in *H. torquatus* by Mathew, 1989). *H. bocconei* Tenore (according to Mathew, 1989, not now a separate species) and *H. multifidus* are characterized by the shape of their leaves as one complex. *H. bocconei* Tenore is the hellebore found in southern and central Italy and its new name is *H. multifidus* subsp. *bocconei*.

The centre of distribution of *Helleborus viridis* L. probably lies in south-west Germany but this species

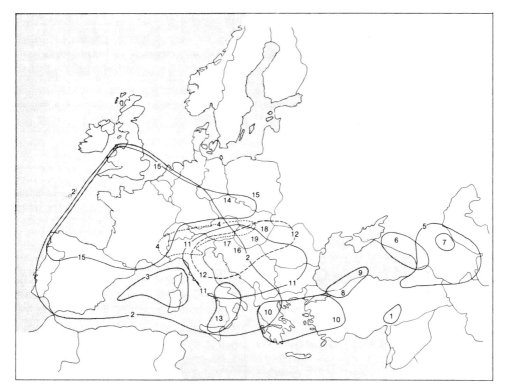

Areas of natural distribution of the European and Eastern species of Helleborus (adapted from E. Ulbrich).

1 = *H. vesicarius*, 2 = *H. foetidus*, 3 = *H. lividus* and *H. argutifolius*, 4 = *H. niger*, 5, 8 and 9 = *H. orientalis*, 6 = *H. orientalis* subsp. *abchasicus*, 7 = *H. orientalis* subsp. *guttatus*, 10 = *H. cyclophyllus*, 11 = *H. odorus*, 12 = *H. multifidus*, including *H. torquatus*, 13 = *H. multifidus* subsp. *bocconei*, 14 and 15 = *H. viridis* subsp. *viridis* in the east, passing to *H. viridis* subsp. *occidentalis* in the west, 16 = *H. dumetorum*, 17 = *H. atrorubens*, 18 = *H. 'Intermedius'*, 19 = *H. purpurascens*.

spreads far to the west and, to a lesser extent, to the east and south. For this reason it is one of those hellebores which, because of their variability, make life very difficult for the enthusiast. In addition to *H. viridis*, *H. niger* L. is found in Germany on the northern side of the Alps, particularly on limestone ridges. The southern subspecies is equally widespread, reaching the Apennines and into northern Yugoslavia.

Helleborus foetidus L. also occurs in southern Germany, but as its centre lies in north-west Spain it is at least questionable whether these are wild plants or have escaped from cultivation, because *H. foetidus* is one of the species used in veterinary medicine in mediaeval times. *H. foetidus* and *H. viridis* are the most widely distributed of all the species, with the possible exception of *H. thibetanus* of which so little is known.

Helleborus argutifolius Viviani is native to only a small area on the islands of the western Mediterranean from the Balearic Islands to Corsica and Sardinia. *H. lividus* Aiton grows only in the Balearic Islands.

MORPHOLOGY

The Seedling

The drawings on pages 17 and 18 show several hellebore seedlings. At this stage all the species look rather similar. They consist of a long root, a hypocotyl, two oval cotyledons with short stems and between them the plumule, the bud from which everything else will develop.

The only seedling that is different is that of *Helleborus vesicarius*. As the drawings show, it is gigantic compared with the others. The immediate thing that strikes a careful observer is the lack of a plumule between the two large cotyledons. The long structure, which at first may be taken to be a sort of hypocotyl, is very soft and sappy compared with that of the other seedlings and extends for quite a distance beneath the surface of the soil; it is like a flat white tube, reminiscent of the lower part of a leek. On either side this underground tube has a shallow groove. If this section is viewed against a strong light, it is possible to see what is hidden in the groove: the plumule sits at the bottom end, shaped like a little flame or the eye of an embroidery needle. In this position it is protected against the heat and drought of the south Turkish summer. The long tube-like structure is nothing more than the greatly elongated 'petioles' of the cotyledons, fused together to form the tube.

All the other species first produce a small true leaf composed of three leaflets from the plumule. This is followed by a second true leaf and possibly one to three more. In the case of *Helleborus vesicarius* these developments were the subject of a note I sent to *The Plantsman* in 1987: 'The seedling ... withers at the onset of the summer drought and forms a sleeping shining white bud at the spot of the needle-like plumula, not quite as big as a pea. Unfortunately the plant, in form of the bud, could not be kept alive. Probably the dormant plant needs more moisture than it did receive. The still alive and particularly branched root seems to prove this. As Brian Mathew said, in October from the bud will grow the first true leaves.'*†

---

* *An edited version of this note was published in* The Plantsman *of September 1988 (Vol. 10, Part II).*
† *In 1992 Brian Mathew germinated six* Helleborus thibetanus. *Germination is hypogeal. The first visible leaf is tripartite. (*The Garden, *Vol. 117, Part II).*

(Left) A, B = seedlings of *Helleborus foetidus*; C = underground part of a two-year-old plant of *H. foetidus*; D = underground part of an older plant of *H. foetidus*; E, F = *H. foetidus* seeds; G, H, J = seedlings of *H. argutifolius*; K = divided outer leaflet of *H. argutifolius*; L = seedling of *H. orientalis* subsp. *abchasicus*: a = hypocotyl with adventitious roots (c), d = the youngest adventitious root, b = the two first true root branches; M = rhizome of a plant of *H. odorus* over two years old: a = part of the rhizome developed from the hypocotyl with numerous adventitious roots (d), b = remainder of main root still present in this stage of development, c = buds that will produce leaves and flower stems in the next year. (Schiffner 1891)

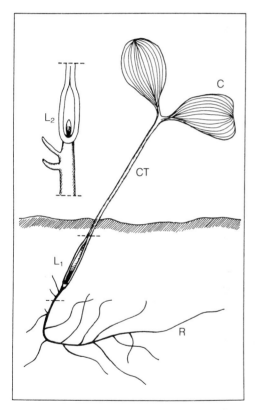 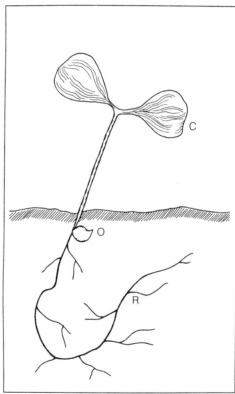

Seedling of *Helleborus vesicarius* I, about 12 cm ($4\frac{3}{4}$ in) tall. C = cotyledons, CT = cotyledon tube, L_1 = leaf bud, L_2 = leaf bud (enlarged), R = root (*The Plantsman* 9, 1: 18).

Seedling of *Helleborus vesicarius* II, about 10 cm (4 in) tall. C = cotyledons, O = over-summering bud (white), R = root. In this stage the above-ground parts of the seedling die back, only O and R remaining alive.

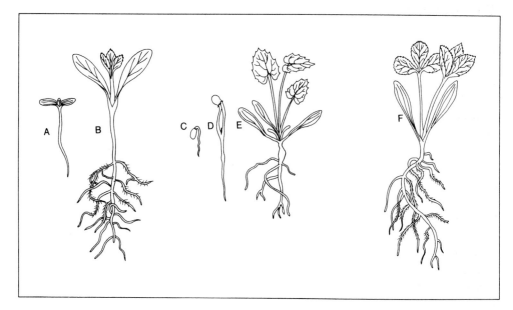

The first true leaves of *Helleborus lividus* and *H. argutifolius* consist of only one leaflet. They become tripartite in the second year and remain so in subsequent years, whereas the leaves of all the other species including *H. foetidus* and *H. niger* will divide many more times, the number increasing with age. From this it would seem that the leaves of *H. lividus* and *H. argutifolius* are the least evolved forms of a hellebore leaf.

The species with radical leaves develop their rhizomes through the

Seedlings. A, B = *Helleborus foetidus*, C, D, E = *H. argutifolius*, F = *H. orientalis* subsp. *abchasicus* (adapted from Schiffner).

lowest part of the stem lying sideways on the soil and producing adventitious roots during the development of the seedling. The stemmed species have no such rhizomes. Their stem branches directly above the roots.

All hellebore seedlings take at least three years to reach flowering size.

The Adult Plant

Underground Parts

In the caulescent (stemmed) species the rhizome of the adult plant is formed by the hypocotyl, which becomes thick and woody, and the lowest part of the first stem. It then grows branches from side buds but does not elongate much underground. The roots grow from the main root as side roots and from the hypocotyl as what are termed adventitious roots.

The main root in the acaulescent (radical-leaved) species dies very soon. Every year new adventitious roots grow from the vigorous new branches of the rhizome, just below the leafy crowns. These crowns develop afresh each year from the terminal leaf buds of the rhizome branches. The previous year's leaves wither away. A branch rhizome probably takes two to three years to reach flowering size. By the time it has fulfilled its purpose, new buds in the axils of the dead leaves may already have grown into new young stems.

In this way the rhizome spreads below ground, but it does not travel far and never grows rampantly. Because of their manner of growth it is easy for the gardener to divide and propagate the species with radical leaves, unlike the stemmed species.

Each year each stem of the caulescent species produces an inflorescence at the terminal, unless it is too weak. Equally regularly, the stem dies completely once the seeds have ripened. Meanwhile a larger number of young stems are already half as tall as the old ones.

The Leafy Part

When the terminal buds of the rhizomes of acaulescent species start to develop, two or more membranous sheath-like structures are the first to appear. Normally these consist of no more than the shortened, broadened petioles, but sometimes they reveal their

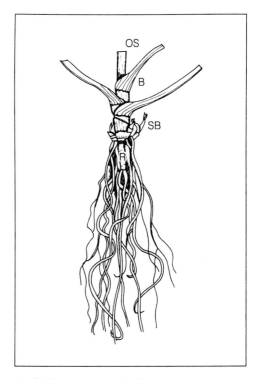

***Helleborus argutifolius*, young rhizome, reduced in size. R = rhizome, SB = shoot bud from which a new stem originates, B = base of leaf, OS = old stem.**

19

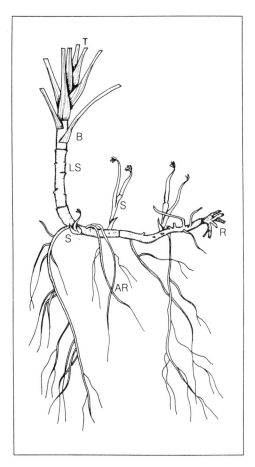

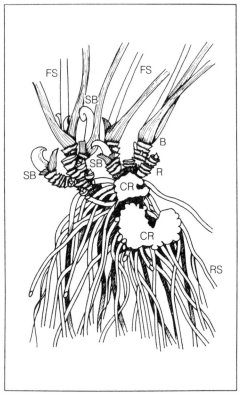

Helleborus foetidus, rhizome and stem, reduced in size. T = terminal bud, B = base of leaf, LS = leaf scar, S = young shoot, R = rhizome, AR = adventitious roots.

Helleborus niger, old rhizome cut in half, reduced in size. B = base of leaf, FS = flower stem, R = rhizome branch, SB = shoot buds, CR = cut rhizomes, RS = roots.

relationship with leaves by carrying a little tripartite blade at the upper end. Following these are the radical or crown leaves, sometimes – as with *Helleborus odorus* – only one, but generally two or more. In the centre of these leaves, at the apex of the rhizome branch, sits the terminal bud. When the rhizome branch is mature, the flowering stem will grow from this terminal bud and then the branch will die. The scars left by dead radical leaves give the rhizome a coiled appearance. It may have one or more dormant buds from which new branches will grow.

The caulescent species behave in the same way at first, growing sheathing leaves or scales as described above at the base of every stem, but these soon die. The lowest third of the stem bears true leaves, which are largest near the base in *Helleborus foetidus* and *H. argutifolius*, gradually decreasing in size as they go up the stem. With *H. lividus* this is not so obvious and at the top it has only two or three leafy bracts, though they still have three leaflets. The appearance of *H. foetidus* is quite different. Here the leafy part of the stem ends abruptly and the green true leaves are replaced by long, pale green membranous bracts that originally enclosed the bud containing the inflorescence. In *H. argutifolius* the reduction in the size of the leaves is particularly noticeable, because as they become smaller, the petioles become shorter. This causes the leaves to be grouped around the

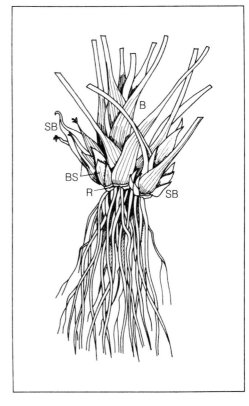

Helleborus orientalis, young plant, reduced in size. B = base of leaf, BS = basal sheaths, R = rhizome, very shortly branched, SB = shoot buds.

inflorescence in the form of a compact, convex dome.

The Inflorescence of the Caulescentes

The inflorescence of *Helleborus lividus* does not develop in the same way as those of *H. foetidus* and *H. argutifolius*, where one large aggregate bud wrapped in membranous scales encloses all the flower buds of one stem. The flowers of *H. lividus* develop in chronological order from the first single bud, which contains a short stem, two almost opposite green bracts, one pedicel with a flower and another pedicel with a bud enclosed by two almost opposite bracts. This bud, when it opens, has the same contents: pedicel, bracts, flower and another bud, and this sequence is repeated as long as the vigour of the stem allows. The bracts of *H. lividus* are not membranous and sheathing, but they have one leaflet and their substance and colour are like that of the true leaves, because they protect the bud for only a very short time and their main function is to assist the inflorescence in photosynthesis.

The inflorescence of *Helleborus lividus* may branch when a second initial bud with an elongated pedicel is produced in the axil of the three-leaflet bracts. When a flower bud is

Diagram showing habit of growth of a plant of the Acaulescentes, in this case *Helleborus multifidus* subsp. *bocconei* (local form *H. siculus* Schiffner). A = long-stemmed cauline leaf resembling a radical leaf, B = radical leaf, C = true cauline leaf.

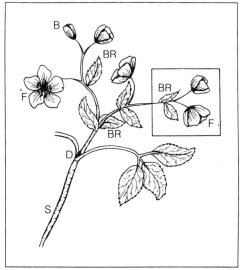

Branching principle of the inflorescence of *Helleborus lividus*. F = flower, BR = bract, B = bud, D = dormant bud, S = stem. The frame encloses one of the modules from which the inflorescence of *H. lividus* is gradually built up.

Developed inflorescence of
***Helleborus argutifolius.* A = stem, B**
= leaf, C = sheath formerly
enclosing inflorescence, D =
inflorescence, E = bracts formerly
enclosing flower.

fully developed, it opens immediately. The tepals remain green until the seed is ripe. The seed on most of the flowers on one plant ripens at about the same time. The flowering period of *H. lividus* lasts from September until the seed is ripe in January or February.

In *Helleborus argutifolius* the inflorescence also develops at the terminal of a leafy stem. At first the whole is enclosed in an aggregate bud around which are wrapped broad sheath-like scales, which are in fact reduced leaves. From this large bud a sturdy, succulent, multi-branched inflorescence develops. Every primary branch arises in the axil of a membranous pale green bract, as do the secondary and lesser branches. At their tips there are a bract, one open flower, and a bud enclosed by two small green bracts. That is the same arrangement, in principle, as in *H. lividus* but in this case it is part of a more complex inflorescence.

On the flowering stem of *Helleborus foetidus* the leaf petioles beneath the inflorescence are also broadened, but they do not become membranous and the blades remain relatively large. Every primary side branch is divided into two equal secondary branches in the same way as the main stem. Each of them sits in the axil of a bract, which is pale green, membranous, long-ovate and acuminate. Between the bases of these twin branches there is a single flower. Each secondary side branch again forks into two and again at the base of the fork there is a flower bud, which is closed. The outer branchlet bears a single bud with two small bracts, while the inner one has the typical division described above, with the single bud in the middle. Every branch and branchlet is subtended by a membranous bract, with the exception of the single buds. These many, broad, membranous bracts enclose the very complex inflorescence from its inception.

As far as the inflorescence is concerned, *Helleborus foetidus* is the most highly evolved species of the genus. Through the repeated forking of its branches it achieves double the number of flowers borne by *H. argutifolius*. *H. argutifolius* falls between *H. lividus* and *H. foetidus*, having attained a complex, better protected inflorescence than that of *H. lividus*, but with only half the flower-bearing potential of *H. foetidus*.

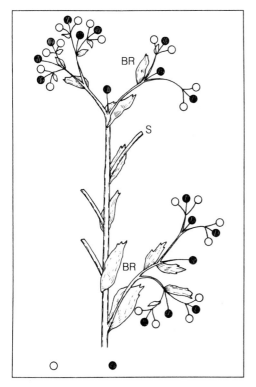

Diagram showing branching
principle of the inflorescence of
Helleborus foetidus. ● = first open
flowers, ○ = flower buds, BR =
membranous, soft, pale bracts, S =
side branch.

Helleborus torquatus. Young
inflorescence.

The Inflorescence of Species with Radical Leaves

The flower stems of the species with radical leaves are not woody at the base and cannot be equated with the stems of the Caulescentes but are, morphologically, the same as a side branch of the inflorescence of a stemmed species. Hence they have only a few branches and bear a maximum of 16 flowers, including a few supplementary buds. As soon as the seed on the normal flowers is ripe, these buds open into tiny flowers 2.5 mm ($\frac{1}{8}$ in) across with the anthers and ovaries reduced to minute green balls. The true flowers are only partly formed in the young inflorescences. Many of them develop later when the first flowers have already opened, as happens with *Helleborus lividus*. As these latecomers do not usually have time to flower in our gardens before the season has finished, it is only possible to discover how many flowers a plant may be capable of producing by growing it under cover in a greenhouse. I have found nine flowers on a stem of 'Atrorubens' ('Early Purple') and a specimen of *H. multifidus* subsp. *bocconei* (formerly *H. siculus* Schiffner) carried 15 flowers plus two supplementary buds.

The bracts (often referred to as cauline leaves) of this group are similar to the radical leaves, and green. The higher up the stem they grow, the smaller the petiole and blade become, but they are never membranous bracts except in *Helleborus niger*.

The True Leaves

The true leaves are very important for determining the identity of the different species; more so, in fact, than the flowers, which are all or nearly all bowl-shaped, whereas the leaves may have very distinct characteristics. This is particularly true of the type plants of each species. The difficulty, however, is that there is usually very considerable variation in the leaves of each species and that there are many intermediate forms between one species and another. This makes it even more important to know the typical leaf forms and to develop a certain instinct for recognizing the species. It is important to the gardener as well as the botanist, because their cultivation needs vary slightly according to where they come from and the species to which they belong.

Clearly the tripartite leaf is the basic pattern for all hellebore leaves. The central leaflet is always separate from the rest, while all the others can be derived from the two outer leaflets since their main veins are mostly branches of the main veins of the outer leaflets. All the leaflets may be divided from the tip downwards but in most cases the division extends no further than half their length.

If the first process described, the division of the two outer leaflets, is rather pronounced, a pedate (foot-shaped) leaf is the result. But if this process is not so clearly visible, the result is called a palmate or hand-shaped leaf. The more primitive

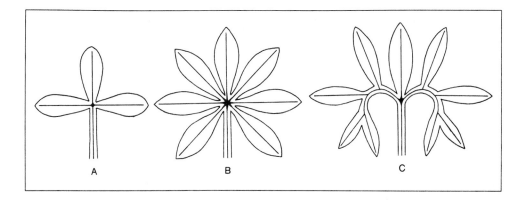

Diagram of radical and cauline leaf-shapes of the genus *Helleborus*. A = tripartite leaf, the least evolved, found in the stemmed *H. lividus*, *H. argutifolius*. B = palmate leaves, which are never the only ones present, but the true form is only seen in young leaves or transitional forms in the Acaulescentes. C = pedate leaves, the most highly evolved among the hellebores. They appear in the species with radical leaves, including *H. niger*, and in the stemmed *H. foetidus*.

leaves of *Helleborus lividus* show a tendency towards this process of division in the asymmetric shape of the outer leaflets. The pedate leaf is very pronounced in *H. dumetorum* and *H. niger*, while the most distinct palmate form is seen in young plants of *H. purpurascens* or some *H. orientalis*. The second process of division, that of the single leaflet from its tip down to the middle, may be very extreme in *H. multifidus*, where the leaflets may be divided into very narrow segments almost to their bases.

The radical leaves of the Acaulescentes are grouped at the tip of each rhizome branch and surround the terminal bud, which is next year's crown. These leaves grow during or soon after the flowering season. Those of the European forms die before the end of the year so these species are said to be 'summer-green'. It would be better to say they are 'leafless in winter' as the leaves stay green until the end of autumn. The leaves of the Turkish Acaulescentes and of *Helleborus odorus* die after flowering, when the new leaves are already growing up, so these are virtually evergreen, as are *H. multifidus* subsp. *bocconei* (*H. siculus*) and, in mild winters, some of the Balkan species.

The Caulescentes bear their leaves on the lowest third of their stems. They grow with the new stem, starting at about the end of the flowering season, stay green during summer and winter, and wither as the stem dies after the seeds have ripened. They are practically evergreen.

Helleborus vesicarius delays the growth of the new stem until the end of August, when the winter rains begin in the Mediterranean area and the essential moisture becomes available. This hellebore is the only one that is truly green all winter and leafless in summer.

The Sheaths

The terminal buds, from which each year's growth is produced, are wrapped in sheaths, membranous scales, which like the bracts are really reduced leaves. They are soft and often almost colourless but may also be reddish or green. In some plants, as for example an old, probably hybrid, offspring of *Helleborus*

orientalis named 'Atropurpureus', these sheaths first develop a tiny tripartite blade and later they grow into 12 cm ($4\frac{3}{4}$ in) tall almost normal radical leaves, forming a small undergrowth beneath the taller true leaves.

The stems of the Caulescentes also grow from buds enclosed by sheaths but, in contrast to the Acaulescentes which retain the sheaths and sometimes even develop them into larger leaves, these sheaths are soon shed and cannot be found at the base of the stems later on.

On some of the Acaulescentes another similarly scaly sheath can be found under the lowest branch, in the area of true cauline leaves or bracts.

The Bracts

The stemmed species have bracts in the area of the inflorescence and the species with radical leaves bear them on the flower stems. They are different in appearance, so it is practical to call the former 'bracts' and the latter 'cauline leaves' to emphasize the difference.

Although the cauline leaves of the Acaulescentes are much reduced true leaves, the blades are still somewhat lobed, small though these lobes may be. The petioles, however, become much shorter and wider higher up the stem, until the leaf is virtually sessile. After that the blade too is progressively reduced, possibly having no lobes and certainly becoming very small in the vicinity of the flowers. As well as giving a degree of protection to a single flower, they help with photosynthesis as they are green, like the true leaves.

The only exception among the Acaulescentes in this respect is *Helleborus niger*. Both its subspecies

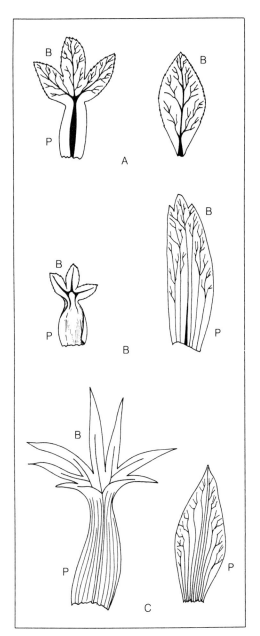

Bracts of the stemmed species. B = blade, P = petiole. A = *Helleborus lividus*. Left: green bract beneath the inflorescences; right: green bract within the inflorescences. B = *H. argutifolius*. Left: green bract beneath the inflorescences; right: membranous, soft, greenish bract with reduced blade within the inflorescences. C = *H. foetidus*. Left: green bract with distinct blade beneath the inflorescences; right: membranous, large, whitish bract within the inflorescences.

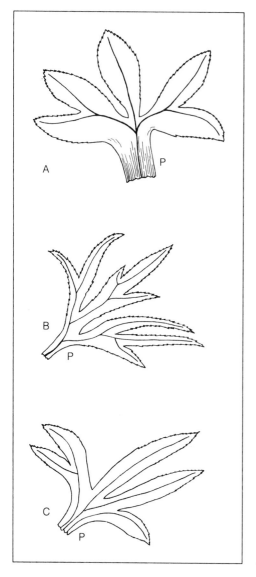

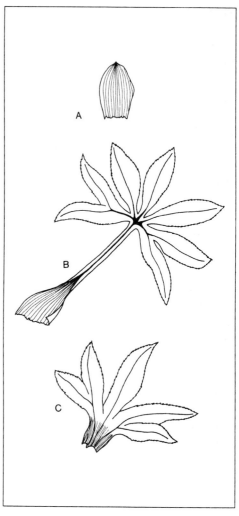

Bracts (cauline leaves) of species with radical leaves I. P = reduced petiole. A = *Helleborus* 'Atrorubens'. B = *H. multifidus*. C = *H. dumetorum*.

Bracts (cauline leaves) of species with radical leaves II. *Helleborus multifidus* subsp. *bocconei* (local form *H. siculus* Schiffner). A = basal, scale-like cauline leaf, light green only at the apex, otherwise colourless. B = basal cauline leaf (bract) similar to a radical leaf, green, veins thin, only the middle rib prominent on the underside. C = cauline leaf (bract) below the first branch on the stem.

have pale, reduced, membranous bracts, not cauline leaves, below the pedicel, similar to the bracts of *H. foetidus* and *H. argutifolius*.

The stem of *Helleborus foetidus* is compressed at the base of the inflorescence and consequently the lower bracts are set very close together. They are greenish-white sheaths but here they seem to be blades that lack chlorophyll. They occur immediately below the start of the inflorescence and at the base of every branchlet, and are soft parts that give good protection to the developing flower stem. The process of reduction has taken place here too, and *H. foetidus* is a classic example of how parts of the plant have evolved from leaves.

The bracts of *Helleborus lividus* have already been described. It is logical that these little ovate leaves are green for photosynthesis, as their protective function lasts for only a very short time. *H. lividus* has very few transitional leaves, those between cauline leaves and bracts.

With *Helleborus argutifolius*, which in cold winters flowers much later than *H. lividus* and *H. foetidus*, the transition to bracts is similar to that of *H. foetidus* in that the aggregate inflorescence bud is enclosed by much reduced cauline leaves and, further up in the flowering part of the stem, there are the same soft, slightly moist bracts as in *H. foetidus*.

Helleborus vesicarius also bears green photosynthesizing organs, not pale membranous bracts. From this the conclusion can be drawn that the flower stem develops, in due course, from a single initial bud as in *H. lividus* and not from an aggregate flower bud enclosed in soft bracts. The sessile cauline leaves are large, much divided, herby and rise above the flowers. Their form and substance are different from those of other members of the genus, especially the stemmed species.

The Flower

The hellebore flower consists of five sepals. Sometimes the two outer sepals differ somewhat in shape and colour from the three inner ones. In rare cases there is a single leaf just below the flower, a transitional form between leaves and bracts. Most of the species have drooping flowers, except for *Helleborus niger* and *H. niger* subsp. *macranthus*, which face sideways, and *H. cyclophyllus* and one of the greenish-yellow *H. orientalis* (syn. *H. kochii* Schiffner), which have nodding or side-facing flowers. The skin of the stem directly below the flower is wrinkled, which enables the flower to alter its angle up or down, for instance after pollination. The flower of *H. vesicarius* is said to face upwards at first and to droop later.

All hellebore species have bowl-shaped flowers of varying depths, but in *Helleborus foetidus* and *H. vesicarius* the mouth of the flower is narrowed, forming a bell, though after pollination these too open to a bowl. The sepals are never shed; they remain until the seed is ripe, but turn green after pollination.

The nectaries are at first flattened cornet-shaped organs, generally shorter and fewer in number than the anthers. They are green or greenish-yellow and very occasionally change colour after pollination. The nectaries of species with radical leaves have incurved lips so that the mouth of the nectary can be closed until the temperature is high enough for bees to be active. They are held

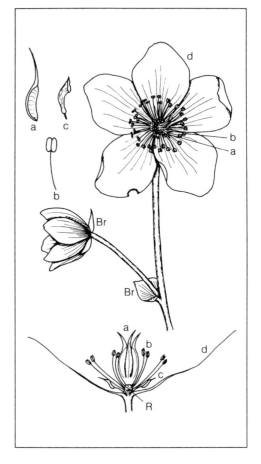

Structure of a hellebore flower. a = carpel, b = stamen, c = nectary, evolved from a petal, d = tepal; R = receptacle, Br = bracts.

on short petioles and have evolved from petals. In the Caulescentes the nectaries are narrowly trumpet-shaped and obliquely cut off. Those of *Helleborus niger* have a long, protracted upper lip like a tongue. The number of nectaries varies from species to species. There may be five as is usual with *H. foetidus*, or up to 20 in, for example, *H. purpurascens*, but it can also differ from one individual to another within a species.

The anthers are held on long, generally whitish filaments and have two sacs, which are elliptic or oblong, coloured cream or yellow. The anthers may be very numerous, possibly as many as 150. Until they are ripe they are clustered in a dense small group around the styles, but during the ripening process the filaments elongate and bend outwards away from the styles, and the sacs open along their inner sides. This outward bending is particularly conspicuous in *Helleborus lividus* and *H. argutifolius*.

The number of styles varies from three to ten, rarely more. The ovary is oblong, flat, slightly curved and keeled on the outer side. A groove runs along the inner side. The keel ends in a long style with a very small stigma. At its small base, and for a short distance at the side, the ovary may fuse with neighbouring ovaries and with the receptacle, or it may have a tiny stalk, as for instance in *Helleborus orientalis* and sometimes *H. cyclophyllus*. In some plants, such as 'Early Purple' ('Atrorubens') the style is free to move during the flowering period.

Helleborus flowers may be different shades of green; white is found in *H. niger* and also *H. orientalis*; true yellow is really the result of hybridization but an approximation to it may rarely occur naturally in *H. odorus* or *H. cyclophyllus*. Some forms of *H. orientalis*, and *H. multifidus* subsp. *bocconei*, have some yellow in their flowers. Pink and red are found in varying intensity, red being sometimes darkened by what is known as an overlying 'bloom' or metallic blue. A lighter slate blue, which is not the result of a 'bloom', can be obtained through hybridization. In addition to the ground colour, hellebore flowers may be decorated with a pattern of lighter or darker, large or small, purple or reddish spots on the flower segments. This is the distinguishing character of *H. orientalis* subsp. *guttatus* from the Caucasus in Georgia.

Fragrance, in so far as it can be detected by the human nose, is not often found in hellebores. Of course *Helleborus odorus*, which owes its name to this feature, is fragrant – sometimes. The scent of blackcurrant or that of elderflower is usually mentioned in this context, not only for *H. odorus* but for *H. dumetorum* as well as *H. multifidus* and *H. cyclophyllus*. If *H. lividus* is brought into the house in winter, one can understand why the bees visit it again and again on their last flights in November, during the last fine days while it stands outside on the terrace. It emanates a very fine, sweet fragrance like that of violets or wallflowers!

The Fruit

The fruit is made up of a number of capsules, corresponding with the number of ovaries that have been pollinated. The nectaries and stamens drop off as soon as pollination has taken place; the flower segments turn green and, as well as the style, remain until the seeds are ripe. In *Helleborus niger*, *H. lividus*, *H. foetidus*, and the other European species, the capsules are fused with the receptacle or with one another at the base for a short distance, even when the seeds are ripe. In *H. orientalis* they are separate from each other and the receptacle, and are attached by their lower tips or very short stems. *H. cyclophyllus* can sometimes be found with fused bases and sometimes with the capsules separated.

The fruit of *Helleborus vesicarius* differs from the rest of the genus in so far as the three to five follicles are much inflated and are fused together for more of their length, so forming a sort of ball about 5–8 cm (2–3 in) in diameter. In this species the styles are much reduced, tiny spikes. The fruit is shed as a whole and carried away by the wind. The walls of the capsules eventually break up and the seed is dispersed.

In all other *Helleborus* species, each capsule opens as soon as it is ripe, splitting on the inner side from the tip down to the base.

Helleborus lividus; small fruiting stem, with swelling carpels (C) supported by persistent tepals (T).

The Seeds

The seeds are attached to the edges of the carpel. The number of seeds varies from ten to twenty. *Helleborus vesicarius* usually has only one or two globular seeds in each capsule, each the size of a peppercorn and light brown or buff in colour. All the other species have glossy black seeds, oblong-cylindrical or shaped like a tiny bean. Later on, when the seed coat has dried, it becomes a dull black.

The ridge or raphe of *Helleborus foetidus* seeds is a conical appendage on the inner side that surrounds the hilum in its centre. In *H. niger* and *H. argutifolius* it has become a spongy, protruberant roll projecting beyond the outer end of the seed, with the hilum at its base.

The seeds of species with radical leaves have a sharp keel that broadens abruptly at the end where the hilum is situated, surrounded by a ridge. The seed coat is leathery; the endosperm resembles horn. In the centre is a very small, barely developed embryo. The seeds of *Helleborus vesicarius*, described above, have a keel and hilum that are scarcely visible.

DESCRIPTIONS OF THE SPECIES

Species with Rhizomes and Radical Leaves

Helleborus thibetanus
Franchet Chinese Hellebore

This can also be found in literature on the subject as *Helleborus chinensis*, which is the only name recognized in the Botanical Garden at Beijing. The plant grows in Gansu, Shaanxi and Sichuan provinces in central China and, as Ulbrich (1938) wrote, has two or three carpels. It is summer-green, with leaves said to be soft and herby, pedate in form with serrate edges. The large white, red or pink flowers are borne singly or in threes on a leafy stem about 30 cm (12 in) tall. There are said to be radical leaves as well as cauline leaves. The nectaries are tubular to funnel-shaped.

Being an inhabitant of shady, damp woods and growing in mossy, moist ground, this plant is probably very tender and would only succeed in cultivation if grown under glass, but it does not appear ever to have been in cultivation, at least not in Europe.

Only a few herbarium specimens exist in Europe: there is, for instance, one in the Botanical Museum in Berlin-Dahlem and one in the Herbar Museum in Paris, both collected between 1883 and 1885. The Royal Botanic Gardens at Kew, more recently, successfully germinated some seeds from Sichuan province sent by a Japanese botanist.

Helleborus orientalis Lam.
Oriental Hellebore,
Lenten Hellebore

This is currently the botanical name for all hellebores with radical leaves and a separate flower stem that are native to Turkey and the Caucasus. Previous writers described several subspecies, classifying them mainly by flower colour. These are no longer considered valid as their other characters are very similar, however important colours may be for nurseries. Although some of these colour forms are geographically closely grouped, there are transitional forms between them and their neighbours, making precise divisions and definitions impossible. Despite this, present-day gardeners will, when talking of hellebores, call those that grow on the Bithynian Olympus *Helleborus olympicus* if they are white-flowered, or *H. antiquorum* if the flowers are pink. If they call a plant *H. orientalis*, they have in mind the greenish- to yellowish-flowered plants, some with outward-facing flowers, which grow from the south-eastern corner of the Black Sea to the southern Caucasus. The dark red *H. abchasicus*, now called *H. orientalis* subsp. *abchasicus*, grows on the east coast of the Black Sea, and the very pretty red-spotted white or pink *H. orientalis* subsp. *guttatus* (Mathew 1989) in Georgia, in the Caucasus.

It is a pity that classification is not as simple as that, for one can find greenish flowers with purple-brown

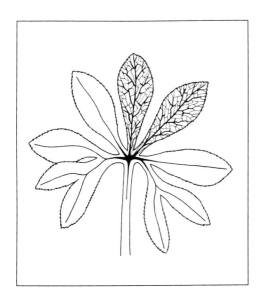

Helleborus orientalis (*H. caucasicus* Braun). Radical leaf, natural size 40 × 40 cm (16 × 16 in).

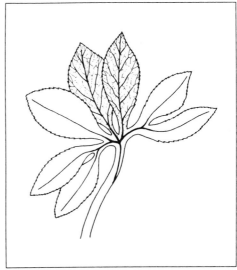

Helleborus orientalis (*H. olympicus* Lindley). Radical leaf, natural size 25 × 16 cm (10 × $6\frac{1}{4}$ in).

spots, or greenish-white ones, among wild populations of hellebores, as well as the lighter pink or red, or pink and green, forms growing on the eastern coast of the Black Sea.

The so-called 'true' species of *Helleborus orientalis* grown in our gardens are at best collected selections vegetatively propagated, because collectors generally choose those they consider to be their ideal of beauty, but it is probable that they have been propagated by seed, and not even hand-pollinated seed, for many years. One can only be certain of growing true geographical colour forms if they are raised from seed collected in the wild from plants that have been reliably identified. The plants will then be true, but will not necessarily live up to expectations, for the reasons mentioned above.

In the same way it is impossible to give an absolutely true description of the morphology of, for example, *Helleborus orientalis* subsp. *abchasicus*, or even one that is true for *H. orientalis* in general, as all of them differ slightly in this and other characters.

An old yellow-flowered cultivar eagerly sought by enthusiasts is grown in some British gardens. It is called 'Bowles' Yellow' and is said to have originated in the garden of E.A. Bowles. It is defined as a selected form of *Helleborus kochii* Schiffner. But what is *H. kochii*? Nothing more than that form of *H. orientalis* that grows south-east of the Black Sea and south of the Caucasus. But there were two forms of this hellebore, known

as *H. kochii hirtus* and *H. kochii glaber*, i.e. the hairy form and the glabrous form. To which does 'Bowles' Yellow' belong? Probably to *H. kochii hirtus*, the leaves of which are slightly hairy on the underside when very young, whereas *H. kochii glaber* has completely glabrous leaves. This example clearly shows how minute the characters used by botanists in the past to divide the species into subspecies, and even forms, are.

The hairy *Helleborus orientalis* grows mainly in the western part of the area of distribution, the glabrous *H. orientalis* in the eastern part; their other synonyms, *H. ponticus* and *H. caucasicus*, are still in use. The flowers of the eastern form tend more towards a milky green-white colour, and those of the western form to brownish yellow, but of course there are no precisely defined areas of these colour forms. One changes gradually to the other. So much for the rather complicated situation regarding *H. orientalis*.

The three to six carpels of 'Bowles' Yellow' are separate at their bases and each has a tiny 'stem', as do all *Helleborus orientalis*. In almost all cases they have large, tough, leathery leaves that last until the end of the flowering season. The ten yellow-green nectaries are flattened, pressed close together, shaped like wide cornets and closed by their incurved lips. The flowers face upwards after pollination. They are held on unbranched pedicels, with cauline leaves divided into three or five parts.

38

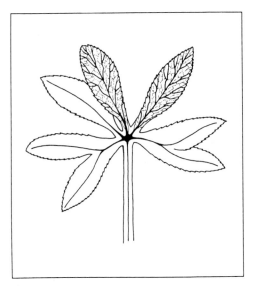

Helleborus orientalis subsp. abchasicus. Radical leaf, natural size 33 × 22 cm (13 × 8¾ in). With the subspecies and forms of the Orientalis group, the size of the leaves and their substance play a valuable role in identification, in addition to the flower colour. The shapes of the leaves indicate only unimportant differences.

The radical leaves may have narrow or broad leaflets and the tepals of the flowers can likewise be broad or narrow. Some plants carry many small flowers, some have tall flower stems, while others hide their flowers among their leaves. The taller forms sometimes masquerade under incorrect names in gardens, for example as *H. cyclophyllus*. *Helleborus* 'Bowles' Yellow' was probably selected because of its clearer yellow colour.

In its native habitats *Helleborus orientalis* flowers all winter, and in some years the species, as well as its hybrids, attempt to do so in gardens. They usually flower around Christmas along with *H. niger* and *H.* 'Atrorubens' ('Early Purple') but sometimes start to bloom in late, or even early, autumn. These early flower stems get frozen in most winters in central Europe and we usually see only the later ones.

The rose-pink hellebore from the Bithynian Olympus, formerly known as *Helleborus antiquorum* Braun, is said to be recognizable by its pointed anthers and the colour of its flowers, similar to that of dog roses. It flowers from the end of March to the beginning of April. A white-flowered form, previously known as *H. olympicus* Lindley, which could be the albino form of *H. antiquorum*, grows in the same region, but is said to be more graceful in appearance. Its anthers are emarginate at their tips. The flower is white, unmarked by any other colour save for perhaps some green. As is clear, the differences are not great and become even less marked in intermediate forms.

The dark red *Helleborus orientalis* subsp. *abchasicus* Braun grows in the Russian province of Abchasia. The best selected forms – it is probable that plants under this name are often seedlings from the original selections – have pretty carmine flowers with waved petals, often finely spotted with a darker colour, and are frequently seen in botanic gardens. The leaves are always glabrous on the underside and are very dark, sometimes even violet-tinted, at the margins. All parts of the plant contain a reddish pigment. The flowers are drooping, held on long pedicels. These plants have been used a lot in hybridizing. It flowers early in its natural environment, beginning in early winter, but in Europe, in years that are not too cold, it starts in late March and ends in April.

What is considered to be the most beautiful hellebore, is the form that grows in the Georgian Caucasus: *Helleborus orientalis* subsp. *guttatus*. The pure subspecies, if there is one, has become rare. It is prone to frost damage and sometimes to fungal disease in some areas. This and *H. niger* 'Praecox' are probably the most tender of all the forms. The ground colour of the flowers is most often white, but cream and pink also occur. The centre of the flower is greenish. In addition, the tepals are spotted purple or brownish-red, with the number and size of the spots and flecks varying and their distribution producing different patterns over the inside of the flower. There are often only a few flowers borne on short stems. Naturally, hybridizers have made many attempts to combine the beautiful markings of this subspecies with good characters from other forms of *H. orientalis*.

Helleborus cyclophyllus Boiss.
Grecian Hellebore

The leaves of an adult plant are large to very large and vary in form, from nearly palmate to pedate. Some of the leaflets are usually divided; from a width of 6 cm (2⅜ in) in the middle, they taper to both ends. The whole leaf is usually circular in outline. Its upper side is rich green in colour, with the underside a little lighter and downy, with prominent veins.

The flowers of some specimens give off a fragrance like honey. The large flowers are a deep bowl-shape and face sideways. They are yellowish green, sometimes with a slight bloom. There can be up to 14 carpels, which are sometimes not united at the base with each other or with the receptacle, but have a tiny stem like *Helleborus orientalis*. The leaves are tough and leathery, but in spite of this fail to survive the majority of winters and are sometimes already dead in October. This is an important feature in distinguishing this species from the yellow-flowered *H. orientalis* and from *H. multifidus* subsp. *bocconei* in its local form *siculus* Schiffner. It is often the latest to flower of all the yellowish-green hellebores, blooming in April-May. This late blooming differentiates it from *H. odorus* and *H. siculus* Schiffner, whilst the shape of the leaves distinguishes it from *H. multifidus* subsp. *bocconei*.

This beautiful species is found only on chalky soils in Macedonia, Albania,

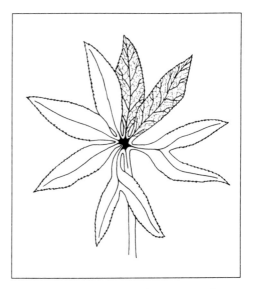

Helleborus cyclophyllus. Natural size 28 × 28 cm (11 × 11 in). A grass-green leaf with matt surface distinguishable from *H. odorus* by these characters and by the circular outline of the blade. Young leaves are distinctly hairy underneath and velvety-soft.

Yugoslavia, Greece and the Greek islands.

Helleborus odorus Waldst. et Kit. Fragrant Hellebore

This hellebore does not always live up to its name, but may smell of blackcurrant. It can usually be distinguished from *Helleborus cyclophyllus* by the fact that a single leaf overwinters on each crown. A plant will sometimes flower as early as February but the normal time is March, in which respect it also differs from *H. cyclophyllus*.

The upper surface of the cauline leaves may be noticeably shiny. The two or three, or in garden conditions perhaps six or more, flowers on each stem are very spectacular in early spring if a good, bright yellowish-green form has been selected, though they may be simply green. The radical leaves are dark green, the underside covered with projecting hairs, which are less silvery than those of *Helleborus cyclophyllus*. Plants that are completely glabrous do sometimes occur, but generally the prominent veins are hairy.

The capsules are fused together at their bases and the eight to 12 nectaries are flat cornets, their mouths having two lips with incurved margins. The fairly large flowers are flat, complete saucers, with overlapping tepals. The usually bifurcated flower stems have very fleshy bases at the start of flowering.

This species grows in the countries bordering the lower Danube, in the Balkans and in upper and central Italy, mainly on chalk. It likes more sun than other hellebores. The form that grows in northern Italy and north-west Yugoslavia has been called *Helleborus odorus* subsp. *laxus* Host. It differs from the type in having fewer leaflets, only five to seven instead of seven to 11, but they may be divided into two to five lobes.

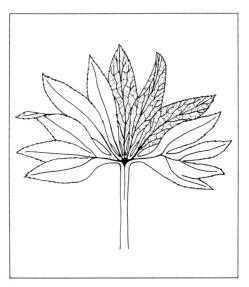

Radical leaf of *Helleborus odorus*, natural size 32 × 17 cm (12¾ × 6¾ in). The leaf is coarsely toothed, the veins project on the underside and are sunken on the upper side. The dark green upper leaf surface is glossy, the underside is paler. The leaf is fairly large.

Helleborus multifidus Vis.
Much-divided Hellebore

This species produces an extraordinary variety of leaf shapes, which is its unique character. There are also transitional forms between this and neighbouring species, which make it very difficult to identify a single specimen with certainty.

When young, the radical leaves are usually hairy underneath. In adult plants they are large and in most cases have 11 to 12 leaflets, though sometimes fewer. These are again divided for at least half their length into three to 12 lobes. Older plants have even more lobes. The number of lobes also depends on the vigour of the plant. A single lobe is narrowly to very narrowly lanceolate, often with a coarsely serrated margin, though this latter character can vary a lot. The overall shape of a leaf is pedate.

The flower stem usually bears many flowers on several branches, but the flowers are only 4 cm ($1\frac{5}{8}$ in) in diameter with the tepals barely overlapping. As a result, the flowers of this species are not among the most spectacular but the leaves, consisting of many narrow segments that sometimes arch downwards, are very conspicuous. They look particularly exotic, like little palm trees, when they are just emerging. Clones that have smaller, more leathery leaves often hold their finely divided blades horizontally, giving a graceful effect.

Helleborus multifidus subsp. *hercegovinus* (Martinis) B. Mathew

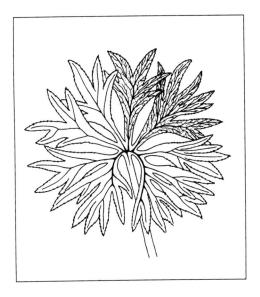

Helleborus multifidus (collected Korita, Yugoslavia, by J. and H. Fuchs). Natural size 29 × 26 cm ($11\frac{1}{2}$ × $10\frac{1}{4}$ in). The similarity with the leaf of *H. multifidus* subsp. *bocconei* can hardly be missed, but the flower is different. Here the division of the leaflets into lobes goes further than in *H. torquatus*. It is carried to extreme lengths in *H. multifidus* subsp. *hercegovinus*.

1989, a pretty plant with leaflets divided into extremely narrow lobes, is found in Hercegovina. *Helleborus multifidus* subsp. *istriacus* (Schiffner) Merxmüller et Podlech, from Istria, is intermediate between *H. odorus* and *H. multifidus*, as is shown by its leaf shape. The leaflets are occasionally completely undivided or divided for only half their length, whereas those of *H. multifidus* subsp. *hercegovinus* are divided right to their bases. The flowers of this

43

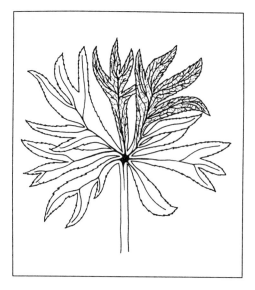

Helleborus (H. multifidus × H. cyclophyllus?), natural size 36 × 30 cm (14 × 12 in). The division of the leaves of this plant, collected by J. and H. Fuchs in Ulag, Yugoslavia, seems to play a joke. In particular, the leaflets to left and right of the central one are as strongly divided into lobes as is generally found only in the two outer leaflets of very pronouncedly pedate leaves, whereas in this case the outer leaflets are rather simple. In addition, these radical leaves are extremely large. Both these characters point to its being a hybrid. Its remaining characteristics place it close to H. multifidus.

subspecies are the same as those of the other subspecies of *H. multifidus*.

The former species *Helleborus bocconei* Tenore, the Italian hellebore, has been classified as a subspecies of *H. multifidus* by Brian Mathew, so it is now called *H. multifidus* subsp. *bocconei* (Tenore) B. Mathew 1989. This subspecies has leaves with five to seven yellowish green leaflets, which are usually divided halfway down into four to five linear, sometimes lanceolate, lobes. Leaflets one and seven have lobes that are again divided. The leaves are similar to those of *H. multifidus*. They are about 20–30 cm (8–12 in) in diameter and are finely hairy, especially when young. The few large drooping flowers look similar to those of *H. odorus*. Their carpels are fused together at the bases. The flowering period of *H. multifidus* subsp. *bocconei*, which grows in central and southern Italy, usually begins in March; its seeds ripen at the end of May.

A form of *Helleborus multifidus* subsp. *bocconei* that grows in Sicily was regarded by Schiffner as a species in its own right and named *H. siculus*. According to Brian Mathew (1989), it is not entitled to species status and is to be included in *H. multifidus* subsp. *bocconei*, but it can be easily distinguished. Among other things, it is remarkable in being green all year, unlike the other subspecies of *H. multifidus* which are, at least in northern Germany, deciduous. It is also possible to observe the development of the terminal buds into new leaf crowns or flower stems in this plant, something that cannot be seen in other members of Acaulescentes as the development takes place underground.

With *H. multifidus* subsp. *bocconei* local form *siculus* Schiffner it has been possible, for three years, to observe that the terminal buds are so elevated that the bases of all its petioles can be seen. Thus the old radical leaves, with their very broad compressed sheath-like bases, lay

widely spread out on the soil surface around the plant when the new growth started. This plant has many leaves, which are leathery but rather thin, and remain green and healthy, provided the winter is not too severe.

During the development of the radical leaves from a terminal bud in the axil of the tallest old leaf, two rather robust, hard sheaths with an obtuse apex develop first. They are reddish violet and slightly hairy beneath, the upper side being whitish. Then the first young leaf follows, upright and tightly furled. Its

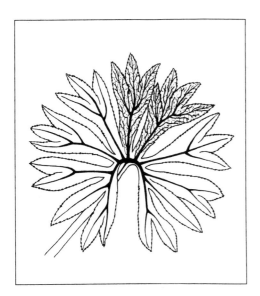

Radical leaf of a *Helleborus multifidus* subsp. *bocconei* from the Apennines. Natural size 26 × 25 cm (10¼ × 10 in).

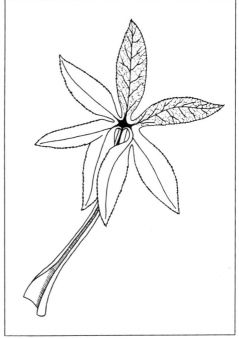

Radical leaf of *Helleborus multifidus* subsp. *bocconei*, local form *H. siculus* Schiffner, a plant clearly distinguishable from *H. multifidus* subsp. *bocconei*.

underside bears a white or almost pink down while the upper surface is light grey-green. The bud of the next young leaf can soon be seen in the axil of the first. In February the down disappears from the underside.

The mature leaf is pedate and has five to seven segments, if the first and fifth, or seventh, leaflets are regarded as single ones. The veins on the underside of the leaves are slightly raised and somewhat hairy; the upper and lower leaf surfaces are smooth, with a soft gloss. By the end of April the petioles are about 15 cm (6 in) tall, with those of the old (and still green) leaves about twice that height. The leaf is 20–25 cm (8–10 in) in diameter, but in poorer conditions it may only reach a width of 10 cm (4 in).

The base of the developing flower stem is also at first wrapped in two sheathing organs, which give way to the terminal bud. The flower stem is somewhat fleshy and reddish at its base. By the end of November it may already be taller than the old leaves, so it cannot be effectively protected in hard winters. At this time of year *Helleborus cyclophyllus*, which can sometimes be mistaken for the Sicilian form, has, for example, hardly any leaves. *H. multifidus* subsp. *bocconei* local form *siculus* Schiffner, though, is in active growth. Its flower stems carry opened cauline leaves and often a side branch. As with the radical leaves, the cauline leaves too have a fine whitish or rosy down beneath and a sheathing base.

At the end of November the first of the greenish-yellow oblong flower buds, hanging on a long pedicel, may open. The flower stem carries seven to 14 medium-sized flowers. The loosely-formed blooms sometimes face sideways but usually droop, starting as convex bells and later becoming flat bowls. They consist of narrow tepals that overlap at the base. The colour of the flowers is a yellowish green, a strikingly spectacular note at this time of year. This colour is maintained for a long time, not turning to green until much later. The pale green carpels are broadly fused with the receptacle and with neighbouring carpels, more obviously so than in any other species. They are slightly inflated at their bases. The persistent styles are erect and about the same length as the capsules. The nectaries are almost open, as their lips are scarcely incurved, and they become a deeper yellow as they age.

The lowest cauline leaf is very near the soil surface and is nearly as large as a radical leaf; the long petiole is particularly conspicuous. According to Schiffner, the second cauline leaf beneath the branch is often formed in the same way, but the plant I studied always had a dry papery sheath at this position. From the axil of this sheath and the thicker main stem a thin side branch often springs. Only about 20 cm (8 in) above this is the first regular cauline leaf, and from its axil a forked stem bearing the inflorescence arises. When it is grown under glass, this plant can bear up to 14 flowers per stem, but in the garden it rarely carries more than seven. By the end of April the flower stem, in the garden, is about 35 cm (14 in) tall. Flowering ends in early May, so the flowering period lasts for an average of three and a half months, sometimes as many as five. As the last flowers are blooming in May, the first seeds are almost ripe.

The plant is tall and slim in shape, taller than it is broad, especially in spring when the old leaves lie flat on the ground and the flower stem has developed. This impression is enhanced by the tops of the rhizomes growing out of the soil until the leaf bases are visible, and by the lower part of the stem, which appears elongated. The long-petioled lower bract and the next sheath seem to be basal elements that have moved upwards. It is almost as if *Helleborus*

siculus Schiffner has developed a short stem similar to those of the stemmed species.

Observations over a long period have shown that a temperature of $-8°C$ ($17\frac{1}{2}°F$) does no damage to an almost fully developed inflorescence in spring, but this most southerly rhizomatous hellebore is, of course, at risk in harsher weather.

Helleborus multifidus, together with its subspecies, is distributed over a very large area from upper Italy to Transylvania, southern Yugoslavia and southern Italy. Many of its members are deciduous in winter, particularly in the more northerly regions. Others remain evergreen in their native habitats. In Central Europe the species flowers from April to May but in mild winters it may be already in flower at the end of January.

Helleborus torquatus
Archer-Hind Serbian Hellebore

The hellebore, which used to be known as *Helleborus multifidus* subsp. *serbicus* (Adamović) Merxmüller et Podlech, has now reverted to its earlier name of *H. torquatus* Archer-Hind. A detailed description appears later in this book in the chapter on Natural Hybrids and Selected Forms under *H.* 'Torquatus'.

That is a beautiful selected form of this species, which has twice been found in the wild, and which differs from the average *Helleborus multifidus* subsp. *serbicus* or *H. torquatus* Archer-Hind only in having exceptionally dark flowers. The type ranges from this dark red through all sorts of greenish-red mixtures, to maroon outside and olive green within and to almost green. These intermediate forms are not really attractive because their flower colours are muddy when compared with 'Torquatus', which is native to southern Yugoslavia and which has now raised all these lesser plants with it to species status as *H. torquatus*. Some earlier writers considered this special Serbian Hellebore to be a form of *H. purpurascens*, but this is unlikely as that species does not occur in Serbia.

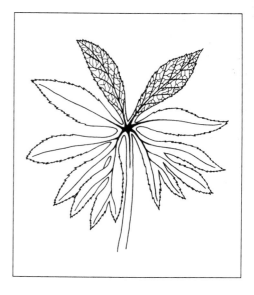

Helleborus torquatus. **Radical leaf, natural size 33 × 25 cm (13 × 10 in) (description under *Helleborus* 'Torquatus').**

**Plate 1 Top left: A self-sown hybrid hellebore in the garden.
Top right:** *Helleborus* 'Frühlingsrose'.

Bottom: A group of *Helleborus orientalis* in a near-natural planting at the foot of a deciduous shrub.

Plate 2 Top left: *Helleborus orientalis.*
Top right: *Helleborus orientalis* hybrid of Eric Smith's 'Zodiac Strain'.
Middle left: A form of *Helleborus guttatus.*
Bottom left: *Helleborus orientalis* hybrid.
Bottom right: *Helleborus orientalis* hybrid.

Plate 3 Top left: *Helleborus purpurascens.*
Top right: *Helleborus multifidus* subsp. *hercegovinus.*
Middle left: *Helleborus orientalis.*
Middle right: *Helleborus bocconei* from Sicily.
Bottom left: *Helleborus cyclophyllus.*
Bottom right: *Helleborus atrorubens.*

Plate 4 Top left: *Helleborus niger* subsp. *niger*.
Bottom left: *Helleborus viridis occidentalis.*
Top right: *Helleborus niger* subsp. *niger* in the wild.
Middle right: *Helleborus niger* subsp. *macranthus*.
Bottom right: *Helleborus odorus*.

Plate 5 Top: *Helleborus foetidus* in the wild.
Bottom left: *Helleborus argutifolius*, the Corsican Hellebore.

Bottom right: *Helleborus lividus*, the Balearic Hellebore, with the inflorescences beginning to develop. Photographed at the end of August.

Plate 6 Top left: *Helleborus* hybrid 'Greencups' (Helen Ballard).
Top right: 'Galathé', seedling from *Helleborus* 'Atrorubens' (Marlene Ahlburg).
Middle left: *Helleborus* hybrid 'Elizabeth Strangman's Pink' (Elizabeth Strangman).
Middle right: *Helleborus* × *nigercors* (originates from a cross made by Elizabeth Strangman).
Bottom left: Selected form 'Torquatus' of *Helleborus torquatus*.
Bottom right: *Helleborus* hybrid 'Ushba' (Helen Ballard).

Plate 7 Top left: *Helleborus* hybrid
with double flower.
Top right: *Helleborus* hybrid 'Black
Knight'. An old German cultivar,
presumably from Max Leichtlin.
Middle left and right: Two
Helleborus hybrids from Heinz
Klose.

Bottom left: *Helleborus* hybrid
'Sylvia' (Helen Ballard).
Bottom right: *Helleborus* hybrid
'Blue Wisp' (Helen Ballard), a
graceful plant with many small
flowers.

Plate 8 Top: *Helleborus* hybrid with unusual, glowing red flower colour. Bottom left: *Helleborus* hybrid (Helen Ballard) with shallow bowl-shaped, sideways-facing flowers.

Bottom right: *Helleborus* × *sternii* F$_2$ hybrid 'Wintersilber' beginning to develop its inflorescence. Photographed at the beginning of September.

Helleborus purpurascens
Waldst. et Kit. Purple Hellebore

Helleborus purpurascens Waldstein &
Kitaibel has almost palmate leaves
and undivided leaflets, at least while
they are young. Later on they are
three- to five-partite, and lanceolate.
On a mature plant the leaf shape is
sometimes reminiscent of *H.
multifidus*. The underside of the
young leaves is flushed brownish-red
and sometimes has soft hairs.

The flowers consist of broad tepals
that overlap at their margins. On the
outside these tepals are violet-purple;
the inside is violet-green, often
suffused with yellowish-brown. The
flower stem is fleshy, short, and often
bears three flowers. The first flower
is already open when the stem is
only 1–3 cm ($\frac{3}{8}$–$1\frac{1}{8}$ in) tall. Its buds
appear very early, looking like little
red peas among the short bracts on
the tiny stem. At the start of its
flowering season the plant looks
rather dwarf, with the flower stems
peering out of the previous year's
leaves, now grey-brown and dry, in
the first half of March. The most
beautiful form, only rarely offered in
the trade, is said to have tepals
purple on the outside and bright
olive green on the inside. The carpels
of this species are fused together at
the base.

Helleborus purpurascens is a
woodland plant. It grows on chalk
soils and is said to be very variable.
The radical leaves die at the end of
winter.

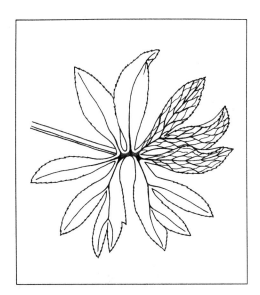

**Helleborus purpurascens. Radical
leaf, natural size 23 × 24 cm (9 ×
9$\frac{1}{2}$ in). The young leaf is often
rather palmate, later becoming as
shown above.**

Helleborus dumetorum
Waldst. et Kit. Hedge Hellebore

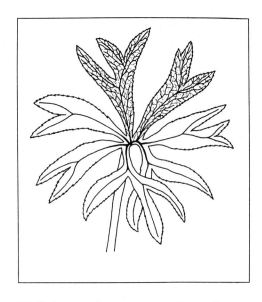

This plant often loses its leaves in winter, but the new leaves develop very early, so that they are almost full-grown when it is in flower. The thin blade is very obviously pedate, about 20 cm (8 in) across. Only the central leaflet – of 11 to 13 – is not joined to its neighbours. The leaflets are broadly linear-lanceolate and have tiny, sharp teeth along their margins. They are dark green, not hairy nor divided into lobes. The flower stem, not much taller than the leaves, is branched and often has multiple (three to nine) flowers. The cauline leaves are particularly large and stand up like hares' ears above the flowers. The shallow flowers are at most 4 cm ($1\frac{5}{8}$ in) in diameter and sometimes give off a faint fragrance; they are yellow-green in colour. The lips of the eight to 12 yellow-green slender nectaries are slightly incurved. According to Schiffner, one of the determining characters for this species is the brownish colour of the carpels after pollination. The seeds are not as

Helleborus dumetorum. **Natural size 33 × 33 cm (13 × 13 in). This leaf is very markedly pedate and has a network of thick veins.**

large as those of other species.

This species is widespread from southeast Austria and Hungary, to Croatia, Slovenia, Transylvania and Romania. It flowers from February to May. There are intermediate forms between this and *Helleborus viridis*.

Helleborus atrorubens Waldst. et Kit. Dark Red Hellebore

Similar to *Helleborus dumetorum*. The flowers of the best selected forms are black-violet outside, while the inside can be light violet or greenish-violet. The leaves have only seven to 11 leaflets. They too die in winter, but the new ones develop only towards the end of, or after, the flowering period. The plant is less robust than *H. dumetorum*.

H. atrorubens likes sunny positions on dry chalky hills and slopes. The dark red hellebore grows in Hungary, Croatia, Slavonia, Transylvania, Bosnia and Serbia. It flowers from March to May.

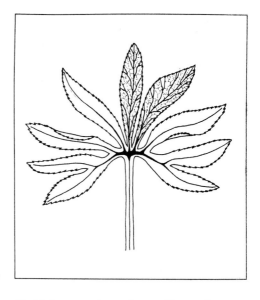

Helleborus atrorubens. **Natural size 30 × 22 cm (12 × 8¾ in). It is finely veined. When young, the leaf has reddish veins. Pedate leaf form.**

51

Helleborus viridis L.
Green Hellebore

Helleborus viridis subsp. *viridis* is indigenous to central Europe and the Alpes Maritimes. Gardeners consider it to be more attractive than the subspecies *H. viridis* subsp. *occidentalis* Reut., which replaces it in western Europe. The two are connected by a wide zone in western Germany and eastern France where transitional forms occur. A somewhat different plant grows in Britain. *H. viridis* is said to be the earliest to flower among its relatives, in the south as early as February, but this does not seem to be true everywhere. The leaves die off very early, in some years as soon as October.

The herbaceous radical leaves of *Helleborus viridis* have a diameter of some 25 cm (10 in) and are rather hard, slightly pedate. They have seven to 11 leaflets, which are not very broad and taper to either end. The three median ones are separate. The margins of *H. viridis* subsp. *occidentalis* are more coarsely toothed than those of subsp. *viridis*. The upper side is a dull dark green and frequently has a slight bloom. The raised veins on the underside are hairy; the relatively small bracts have a sheathing petiole. The flower stem is tall, scarcely branched and generally carries three flowers. The nodding flowers, held on long, angled pedicels, are relatively large. Their colour is silvery green and the best selected forms have a waxy bloom. The anthers are noticeably

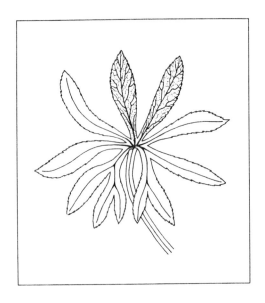

Helleborus viridis subsp. viridis (from western Germany). Natural size 20 × 20 cm (8 × 8 in). This leaf is smaller than that of *H. viridis* subsp. *occidentalis* and also a paler green. Its margin is not noticeably toothed. *H. viridis* subsp. *viridis* dies back especially early and quickly and shoots in spring earlier than *H. viridis* subsp. *occidentalis*.

longer than the yellow-green nectaries and the green styles carry almost erect stigmas. Three to five large inflated carpels are clearly fused at their bases.

The subspecies *Helleborus viridis* subsp. *occidentalis* has leaves that are about 20 cm (8 in) across and have nine to 11 leaflets, which are more coarsely and also more irregularly toothed than those of subsp. *viridis*. Additionally, they are lighter green and have no bloom. The whole shape of the leaf is noticeably round, and

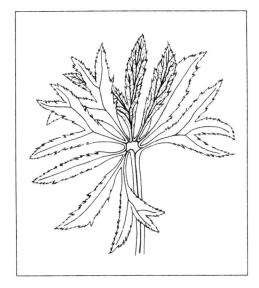

Helleborus viridis subsp. occidentalis (from Andorra). Radical leaf, natural size 30 × 26 cm (12 × 10¼ in). This subspecies has leaf margins remarkable for their strong and manifold serrations and fine leaf veins. Only the central vein is prominent beneath. The leaf is dark green and particularly striking when young.

the tips of the leaflets often droop.

At the start of the flowering season the flower stem is only 20 cm (8 in) tall but later on it grows taller. The cauline leaves are very large, unlike those of *Helleborus viridis* subsp. *viridis*. It also differs in that its three to four flowers are smaller in size and their pedicels are longer. The generally round tepals overlap at their bases. Their colour tends towards yellow-green and there is no bloom. The carpels are shorter and more strongly fused.

As it is very difficult to tell the green-flowered European hellebores apart, the differences between the type species are summarized as follows, according to Schiffner:

Helleborus viridis differs from *H. odorus* in that it never overwinters and also has smaller, herbaceous leaves, the outer tips often drooping; it has narrower, less hairy leaflets and unscented, sometimes bluish, flowers of smaller size. It differs from *H. multifidus* by the only occasionally dissected leaflets and the more blue, or sometimes whiter, colour of the flowers and blue-green leaves. *Helleborus dumetorum* is more yellow-green, its leaves have a shiny upper surface, are glabrous beneath, and are not dissected. The generally well-budded flowering stems are overtopped by large bracts, the flowers are smaller and have very narrow tepals.

Helleborus niger L.
Christmas Rose, Snow Rose

Everyone knows this hellebore, at least in its form 'Praecox', which is the Christmas Rose. Less well known is the fact that *Helleborus niger* has two subspecies, *H. niger* subsp. *niger* L. and *H. niger* subsp. *macranthus* Freyn. It is quite important to know which of the two subspecies one has in the garden, as they differ in some respects.

The rhizome of *H. niger* subsp. *niger* appears coiled, due to the scars left by dead radical leaves. The rhizome branches are about 10 cm (4 in) long. On each branch there are a few sheaths and following these, up to three radical leaves and a flower stem. The petioles are thick and fleshy, dotted or finely striped with red at the base. The leaf blade is very obviously pedate, made up of seven to nine broadly wedge-shaped leaflets with coarsely toothed margins, the teeth pointing towards the apex of each leaflet. These teeth are not spiny. The grass-green, slightly glossy leaves are thick and leathery in substance, and smooth. The rounded flower stem is generally as tall as, but sometimes a little taller than, the leaves. It very often bears only one flower, sometimes two.

Helleborus niger differs from all the other radical-leaved species in its bracts, which have no chlorophyll and no blade. They are whitish, membranous and untoothed. It seems probable that they have evolved by the broadening of the petiole and are therefore rather small. They grow at

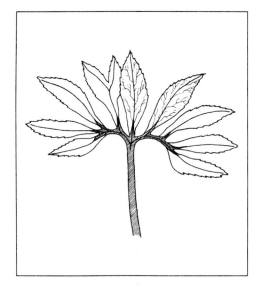

Helleborus niger subsp. niger 'Praecox'. Radical leaf. The most obvious character of this subspecies is the shortness of the petioles and the grass-green leaf colour (whereas the leaf of H. niger subsp. macranthus is almost twice as tall and large and very dark blue-green). The substance of the leaves is leathery and the upper surface is smooth. The form is very pronouncedly pedate. The leaf petiole is shorter than the flower stem, about 20 cm (8 in) tall.

the base of a potential pedicel; even when there is no flower, they are always to be found here.

The flower is made up of large ovate tepals with overlapping margins. The snow-white flower may have a reddish flush on the outside, but can also be entirely snow-white or slightly greenish. When the nectaries and anthers have fallen, the tepals become a dirty white flecked with red, or sometimes turn green. The nectaries are tubular, 12 mm ($\frac{1}{2}$ in) long, and have a long upper lip projecting straight forwards, while the lower lip is only a small one. *Helleborus niger* has a great many anthers, which at first are bent inwards but curve sharply outwards when they are ripe. They carry lemon-yellow pollen. The pistils, up to 10 in number, consist of small, scarcely keeled ovaries with styles of the same length. The ovaries develop into capsules, which taper to the base and are attached to a rather large, conical receptacle. Their bases are fused at the inner side and the capsule bends outwards; the styles too bend in this direction. The shining black, almost cylindrical seeds have a deep hilum groove and a big, spongy, white elaiosome on the lower side.

Helleborus niger subsp. *niger* grows, like *H. niger* subsp. *macranthus*, at the margins of both deciduous and coniferous woods. As our gardens are generally similar in character to this type of landscape, the plants feel at home there as they do in their natural habitats – if gardeners do their best for them.

The second subspecies, *Helleborus niger* subsp. *macranthus*, differs from the first in having narrower leaflets with smaller teeth at the margins that are sharp spines. The leaves are a dull bluish-green. The flower frequently has narrower, acuminate segments and the styles are longer than the stamens. There are often three flowers to a stem. The plant is larger and more robust than *H. niger* subsp. *niger*. During the flowering season the large leaves often spread outwards in such a way as to surround the flowers like a garland. *H. niger* subsp. *macranthus* flowers later in gardens than *H. niger* subsp. *niger*, namely from January to March.

Helleborus niger subsp. macranthus. Radical leaf, natural size 36 × 21 cm (14$\frac{1}{4}$ × 8$\frac{1}{4}$ in). The petiole is 33 cm (13 in) long. The blade of the leaflets is more distinctly distant from the base of the central rib than in H. niger subsp. niger, thereby making it appear to be 'petioled'. The petiole and the midribs of the leaves are darker. The petiole stands more erect, so that the leaf-blade is often above the flowers. The substance of the leaf is markedly thicker than that of H. niger subsp. niger 'Praecox'; the form is strongly pedate. In other respects the plants are very similar.

The flowers tend to be more variable. On the reverse, the tepals are more frequently flushed with a deeper pink. The flower shape is flat or like a bell, the tepals can be wide and round or longer and acuminate, and slightly waved.

The true subspecies are very rarely found in gardens today. They have long since interbred with each other. The resulting plants tend towards *Helleborus niger* subsp. *macranthus*, which makes them strong robust plants.

Helleborus niger subsp. *niger* is found on the northern side of the Alps, particularly in limestone regions, whereas *H. niger* subsp. *macranthus* grows on the southern side and also in the Apennines and the northern Balkan highlands. Where their areas meet, intermediate forms are, of course, to be found.

The old *Helleborus niger* 'Praecox' is a selected form of *H. niger* subsp. *niger*, chosen for its very early flowering. This cultivar starts to show its first flowers at the end of September and beginning of October, is then usually interrupted by wintry weather and produces a further flush of bloom in January to February, but at that time of year it is outshone by later-flowering forms of *H. niger* subsp. *niger* and after that by *H. niger* subsp. *macranthus*. As has been said, almost all plants available commercially today are hybrids and therefore the flowering season varies widely, especially among seedlings from these hybrids. It is, however, well worthwhile selecting seedlings

with the aim of getting a long flowering period.

In the garden the Snow Rose or Christmas Rose is most effective when it is thoroughly established. Given good cultivation, it becomes more and more beautiful with age, and never threatens to overwhelm its neighbours.

The old leaves of the previous summer gradually wither during the winter and in April, after flowering, they are replaced by fresh ones. *Helleborus niger* 'Praecox' is an exception in that it produces new leaves from the beginning of July.

It is, incidentally, fascinating to watch the progression of growth of flower stems and leaves under cover in a frost-free situation and under artificial light. *Helleborus niger* differs from most other hellebores in the manner in which these parts emerge from the soil. As soon as the carpels are swollen and the tepals have turned green, new leaves push through the soil surface. They do this in a similar way to French beans. The upper end of the petiole, just below the leaf base, is thinner than the lower part and sharply bent like a hairpin. It is also different in colour, being red-brown, and the skin is peculiarly wrinkled. The leaf segments are folded together like an umbrella about to be put into its cover and are also furled like an umbrella, so forming an acute tip. The wrinkled neck of the petiole pushes through the soil surface and then straightens, pulling the leaf out of the soil. The flower stem emerges in the same way. Most other members of the genus do not behave in this curious way. It possibly has something to do with the exposed habitats and early flowering period of this species. As far as the flower stem is concerned, this behaviour may be connected with the fact that the flower is not protected by being enclosed in bracts.

Species with a Surface Stem

Helleborus lividus Ait.
Balearic Hellebore

As its name indicates, this hellebore is native to a very restricted area, namely the Balearic Islands. *Helleborus lividus* is not hardy in most gardens as the upper parts are regularly killed by frost at about −5°C (23°F), though the underground parts are never damaged. Experiences over eight years have shown that they can withstand temperatures down to at least −25°C (−13°F). However, the plant remains the size of a two-year-old seedling. How long a plant can exist in this way is, to date, unknown.

Ulbrich believed that in our gardens *Helleborus lividus* needs six to seven years to reach flowering size. That is obviously not the case: it needs no longer than other species. He probably grew his plant in the open and in its seventh year it experienced its first mild winter and so was able to flower at last.

The seedlings are easily recognized as their cotyledons are long and narrow with conspicuous white veins. Until the advent of frosts, this plant can be grown in a large pot in the open, where it develops its characteristic beauty better than under glass. The colour of the leaves varies from grey-green with a grey bloom on both surfaces, to blue-green above and a rosy colour beneath, in which case the reverse and sometimes the inside of the flowers, and even the flower stems, also have this pretty pink colouring. The adult leaves, in addition, are marbled with white veins. More often, the flowers are yellowish green inside with a bluish bloom. Several of these bowls are carried on branches at the upper end of each stem.

Unlike the flowers of the other two Caulescentes, they do not develop simultaneously while protected by a group of bracts, but grow in succession, one bud following another. Each fully developed flower bud opens immediately, so the inflorescence begins with a single flower, which develops in the axil of a bract. Another bud, enclosed by two tiny bracts, grows in the axil of a second bract, which is opposite the first. From this bud come, again, two opposite bracts, one flower, and a bud enclosed by two tiny bracts, which continues the formation of the inflorescence, following the same principle. The bracts are green from the outset, never pale and membranous. In this manner a branched inflorescence gradually develops, with the branches becoming more robust as time passes. Occasionally, depending on the vigour of the plant, additional bud complexes may grow in the axils of bracts.

The flowers have a faint sweet fragrance of violets or wallflowers, only detectable by the human nose when the plant is grown under cover. In the open this fragrance never fails to attract bees from the end of August until frosts begin. In the garden the flower stems will be killed if the temperature drops to about −5°C (23°F), but indoors the plant will flower until mid-February.

As Viktor Schiffner described the rhizome very thoroughly but not those parts of the plant above the ground, I want to make up for this with my own record of observations. These observations were made in the middle of February, at a time when all the flowers, except for three buds, were over or open:

The plant, overwintered under artificial lights, is in its second season of flowering. It consists of a large stem that grew after the previous flowering season and three little stems that developed later while in its winter quarters. It is of the cultivar 'Pictus' but at this time of year there is no sign of the pinkish colouring on the reverse of the flowers and leaves, and none of the bluish blooms remain. The leaves on the main stem are changing to yellowish green, while those of the little stems are still the normal green. The younger stems emerge from the soil immediately beside the main stem.

The bottom 18 cm (7 in) of the main stem has no leaves left on it. The large leaf scars almost encircle the stem and the internodes between them are 6 cm (2⅜ in) long. From the base, which is only the thickness of a pencil, the stem gradually becomes thicker and the internodes shorter. Above 18 cm (7 in) the leaves are still present, growing so closely together that their petiole bases seem to rise one from another.

They grow in spirals around the stem. In the axils of the leaf scars are fairly plump dormant buds. The leafless part of the stem is purple-brown. This colour becomes lighter higher up the stem; the petioles too are coloured halfway up, but the youngest branches of the inflorescence are only green. This may be different in the open in natural habitats.

Beneath the inflorescence the main stem has five leaves. The petiole of the lowest is 14 cm (5½ in) long, that of the highest is 7.5 cm (3 in).

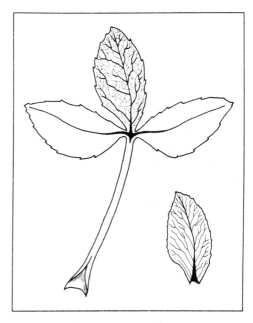

Helleborus lividus. **Stem leaf, natural size 25 × 19 cm (10 × 7½ in), green bract. Stem leaf and bract have the same very firm, leathery, smooth substance. The strong veining is whitish, making the leaf appear marbled. Its reverse is light reddish-brown.**

59

The stem-clasping bases of the lower petioles become smaller and the petioles are rounded. Gradually they become channelled and are even broadly winged at the lower part of the inflorescence where bracts start to appear.

The leaves are composed of three leaflets. The central one is symmetrical. The two outer ones are divided by their main vein into two unequal parts. The inner part is narrow, the outer broader with an abrupt outward curve at the base. The leaflets of the lowest leaf are 15 cm (6 in) long and 7 cm (2¾ in) wide, more or less oblong or ovate in form, acuminate at the tip, and their bases taper into shortish petioles. The highest leaves are still quite large, 10 cm (4 in) by 4.5 cm (1¾ in).

The stem of the inflorescence grows from the axil of the topmost leaf. On one side is another flower stem that has grown from a supplementary bud such as is found on younger inflorescences. Both these stems divide again after 1 cm (⅜ in), and the main stem forks again 3 cm (1⅛ in) further up into two almost equal, long, flowering branches that become gradually thinner. At intervals of about 9 cm (3½ in) they bear two opposing bracts, which are placed almost level. From the axil of the upper one a pedicel about 5 cm (2 in) long, with a flower, grows; from the axil of the lower one another bud develops which contains the same sequence, namely two bracts, pedicel with

flower, another bud, and so on until the end of the flowering season.

The first, lower bracts still consist of three leaflets and a winged petiole, but they are followed by longer bracts with two segments only. Gradually the later ones have unwinged petioles and become more and more sessile bracts that show clearly the serrated edge, green colour and substance of a true leaf. This demonstrates that they have not been developed from the petiole but from the leaf blade. Two-thirds of the way up the last small branch of each stem of the inflorescence sit two little green bracts with serrated edges, below the terminal flower. Now and then, in a fork of the flower stems or in the axil of a supplementary bract, there may be a plump dormant flower bud, but if the inflorescence can build up, following its usual course of development, this bud does not grow. These dormant buds are probably held in reserve in case the other buds are destroyed.

The stem at first slants outward from its base and, together with the flower head, has a total height of about 65 cm (26 in). The plant is about 60 cm (24 in) in diameter.

The older of the two small stems that grew up later in the winter has a flower stem with two branches above four true leaves and to date has lost none of its leaves. It is 35 cm (13¾ in) tall, bearing ten flowers and three buds, and has not yet finished growing. The main stem has 30 flowers plus two dormant buds. Seeds on the first flowers ripened four weeks ago. Further hand-pollinated seeds are developing, whereas those flowers not hand-pollinated have not set seeds. This shows that the plant is self-fertile but has no mechanism for self-pollination.

The flowers, which out-of-doors and early in the season are an attractive blue-green and pink, are now a bluish yellow-green and seem to have become smaller under artificial light. They consist of five equal tepals that form a complete bowl and last until the seeds are ripe, then immediately go brown and die. At the beginning of the season an individual flower was 5.5 cm ($2\frac{1}{8}$ in) in diameter but now, at the end, it is only 4 cm ($1\frac{5}{8}$ in).

Ten to 12 nectaries (open, curved tubes that are in fact transmuted petals) contain the nectar. Their rims are slightly toothed and they are yellow-green, about 1 cm ($\frac{3}{8}$ in) long. Forty to 50 white filaments carry cream anthers with pollen of the same colour; at first they form a closed head around the ovary. As the flower matures, the circles of stamens bend outwards, one after another. The filaments grow longer during this process, until they are nearly as long as the carpels which, at the beginning, were one-third longer. The nectaries and stamens are shed as soon as pollination has taken place or when the flower dies. Tepals and ovaries of a pollinated flower become green and aid the developing seeds by extra photosynthesis.

The six carpels are about 1.7 cm ($\frac{5}{8}$ in) long and consist of the ovary, 0.7 cm ($\frac{1}{4}$ in) in length, and the 1 cm ($\frac{3}{8}$ in) long style with the stigma, a very small knob inclined outwards. The lower end of the style runs out into a keel on the outer side of the ovary. Each ovary is fused with its neighbours at the base. They stand on top of a succulent conical receptacle. As ripening progresses they become longer and fatter, and change from light green to a sandy colour. The outside of the capsule has narrow horizontal stripes. The style remains until the capsule opens along its inner side and releases the seeds, which have been attached to the placenta on both sides of the inner opening. The seeds are 5 mm ($\frac{1}{4}$ in) long and 2–3 mm ($\frac{1}{10}$ to $\frac{1}{8}$ in) broad, glossy black with a whitish raphe.

After the seeds have ripened the old stems dry off, but by that time new stems have begun to develop, at first showing no sign of the flowers to come. These stems grow and expand in the course of the summer and in August they begin to form the inflorescences and to throw up more new stems.

Helleborus lividus will cross with *H. argutifolius*. The resulting plants are named *H.* × *sternii* after Sir Frederick Stern, the first person to make the cross, and are themselves fertile. *Helleborus lividus* is also fertile with *H. niger* but this cross produces infertile hybrids that are intermediate between the two parents in appearance but are always stemmed plants. (See also the very similar hybrid *H.* × *nigercors*.)

Helleborus argutifolius Viv.
Corsican Hellebore

Helleborus argutifolius Viviani (formerly *H. corsicus* Willd.) is remarkably different from *H. lividus*, as can be seen from the descriptions of the inflorescences. However at first sight the relatively hardy, semi-woody stem with its similarly-formed leaves has much in common with *H. lividus*.

The stem is 1.3 cm ($\frac{1}{2}$ in) in diameter and the height to the base of the actual inflorescence is 45 cm ($17\frac{3}{4}$ in). About six of the lower leaves have already died when the flowering season begins. The internodes become shorter and shorter higher up the stem. The true leaves form a convex dome, about 50 cm (20 in) in diameter, beneath the inflorescence. Their petioles become successively shorter as they rise up the stem; that of the lowest remaining leaf is 15 cm (6 in) long while the last one, which is already broadened, is only 1 cm ($\frac{3}{8}$ in) in length. After that the petioles change into bracts by broadening; the remainder of the blade is visible only as a toothed rim around the one-piece bract. The first green bracts with what might be called totally reduced blades and very wide petioles (or perhaps central veins) are the bud sheaths enclosing the inflorescence, which is very much compressed while it is in the bud.

The central stem of the inflorescence and its branches are light green and fleshy. The internodes at the base of the inflorescence are barely 5 mm ($\frac{1}{4}$ in) long. When the bud containing the inflorescence opens, the central stem lengthens and by the time all the first flowers on the main stem and side branches are open, the inflorescence is 15–17 cm ($6–6\frac{3}{4}$ in) long. The first flowers to open protrude from the inflorescence on bent, angled pedicels. The open flower is 4.5 cm ($1\frac{3}{4}$ in) in diameter. It is light green in colour, both outside and inside, and forms a bowl in which many stamens with cream pollen can be seen surrounding, as a rule, four carpels, and bending outwards rather untidily. The inflorescence I observed had nine primary branches (the final situation during seed ripening will be described later in this section).

The lowest remaining leaves measure about 22 × 12 cm ($8\frac{3}{4}$ × $4\frac{3}{4}$ in) and consist of three leaflets of a leathery texture with coarsely toothed margins. The upper side of the blades is a glossy green, while underneath they are paler with a dull surface. Only the central vein of each leaflet is prominent on the underside. The petiole is light green and deeply grooved, the groove being noticeably broadened in the compressed central part of the stem so that the leaf base clasps half the stem's circumference. In this part of the stem the petioles seem literally to be stacked one on top of another, they grow so closely.

In early May the wide base of the seed-bearing part of the upper stem stands among the short, broad, green bracts described above, which previously enclosed the bud. At the base it is very much compressed, giving the impression that the main stem and its branches rise from a common platform. Here there are two small branches carrying buds, of which the uppermost are still closed, though all the rest of the flowers are over. The lower, large floppy bracts within the inflorescence start to turn brown, as do the unpollinated flowers. Those that have been pollinated are light green with pale green carpels, which are steadily swelling. The main stem is the longest; the side branches become shorter as they go down the stem, so the whole inflorescence looks like a bouquet.

The inflorescence I observed contained 60 pollinated flowers, six unopened buds and two short side branches with buds. Even in this state the stems of *Helleborus argutifolius* are very effective in the garden. In spite of being a rather coarse plant, from a distance it gives the effect of a billowing green cloud.

In early May the new stems are about 30 cm (11⅞ in) high. The lowest leaf, a simple green scale, is a 10 cm (4 in) long grooved petiole or broad central vein without a blade, which ends in an acute apex. The next two or three leaves have relatively small blades, but higher ones become larger until the full size is attained. All are, at this stage, rather soft, but sharply toothed and wrapped closely around the stem. Each individual stem bears a terminal bud, which at this time of year does not look anything like a flower bud.

***Helleborus argutifolius*. Stem leaf, natural size 13 × 13 cm (5⅛ × 5⅛ in). The leaf margin is strongly and spinily toothed. The veins are light green, translucent, finely netted, prominent on the underside of the leaf. The leaf-blade has a very firm, leathery substance and its upper surface is smooth.**

Helleborus foetidus L.
Stinking Hellebore

The centre of distribution of this species lies in Spain, so it is the most westerly member of the genus and is widely distributed from central Germany to France and Britain. In spite of inhabiting this large area it has developed only a few variants. The colour of the stems and petioles may be red instead of green; the leaves are sometimes a metallic blue-green; they are said occasionally, but very rarely, to have fissured margins. The flower is always the same; it can, however, have a sweet fruity scent.

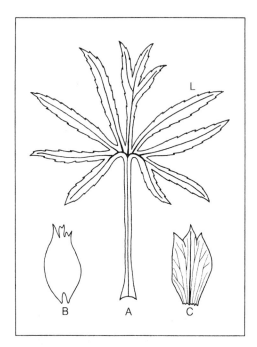

Helleborus foetidus, **English form. A = stem leaf, natural size 21 × 18 cm (8¼ × 7 in); L = very narrow leaflets; B and C = bracts, B = whitish, C = greenish.**

The lower half of the stem, which is thinnest at the base, bears the beautifully cut true leaves, which caused the famous gardener Karl Förster to give it the much more appropriate name of Palm-Leaf Hellebore. This is a far better name as at no time does this plant stink. Only if the leaves are crushed do they give off a peculiar smell, like something cooked or fried. The leaves are pedate, composed of about nine very narrow lanceolate segments, which are not usually dissected from the apex.

The upper part of the adult plant or stem consists of the inflorescence. This develops from the end of August from a small light green bud, at first tightly closed. By November it is large, fairly long and club-shaped. It is enclosed in many long, soft, membranous and very pale bracts and often, at this time, it bends to one side. In December the now upright inflorescence is complete in so far as the side branches have expanded in all directions with many buds and bracts on thick, fleshy stems, but the buds have not yet opened. This happens very gradually through the whole of winter and well into spring, depending on the weather.

The flowers grow from the axil of a membranous bract. They open in succession from the lowest to the highest. One stem may bear up to 100, or even 150, flowers each 1–3 cm ($\frac{3}{8}$–1$\frac{1}{8}$ in) in diameter during the flowering season. These are not open bowls, but bells with a narrow mouth with red colouring at the margins of the tepals; immature flowers lack this colouring. The one to three carpels are fused at their bases; the funnel-shaped nectaries are yellow-green and bent. The black seeds have large conical elaiosomes. After pollination the flowers open out to a flaring bowl shape.

The true leaves support the adult plant by having a flexible joint at the base of the petiole. Petioles and leaves bend downwards and the leaf tips rest on the soil surface.

An old plant has a number of stems but these live for only one year as they die once the seed is ripe. Meanwhile, a larger number of young stems has grown up and these will mature and flower in the coming season. In this way each stem grows, flowers and dies in the course of a year, unlike the crowns of the species with radical leaves, which need two to three years to mature to the flowering stage. This three-year cycle is seen only in young plants of the stemmed species as they need three years to develop from seedlings to adult plants.

Helleborus foetidus is fairly drought-resistant and can be planted almost anywhere in the garden. Unfortunately the inflorescence is rather easily damaged by frost. In a good spot this plant has considerable garden value in both summer and winter. The British native form has less to recommend it than the southern form, as its narrow leaflets and long petioles and stems make it look rather gawky.

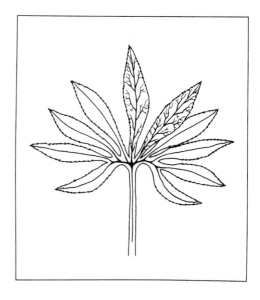

Helleborus foetidus, southern form. Stem leaf, natural size 26 × 22 cm (10¼ × 8¾ in). Leaflets relatively wide and dark blue-green, with a metallic sheen.

Helleborus vesicarius. A = young plant at the start of the flowering season, B = stem with ripe seedpods, C = shapes of tepals, D = stamen, E = pistil, F, G = nectaries, side and front views, H = half-ripe carpel with style still upright, J = seeds. (Schiffner 1891).

Helleborus vesicarius Auch.
Bladder Hellebore

This hellebore is an outsider among the species. It is restricted to a comparatively small area in south-east Turkey and northern Syria. There it grows at an altitude of 700–1,000 metres (2,300–3,200 feet) in open maquis on chalk. A number of growers have this species in cultivation; a few have managed to get seeds to set.

Helleborus vesicarius grows to a height of about 50 cm (20 in) and consists of erect stems with many herbaceous leaves. According to Brian Mathew, it is hardy in southern England in protected places. Seedlings will not survive a hard winter, but adult plants can be grown in sheltered places with winter protection.

The small flowers are bell-shaped and green, and similar to the flowers of *Helleborus foetidus* in having tepals that are green with red-brown edges. In the literature it is said to lose its tepals after pollination, but according to Mathew in *The Plantsman* of December 1986, this is untrue. Stamens and tubular nectaries are shed, as with all hellebores. The three carpels grow and inflate enormously after pollination, and are fused together for half their length. This bladder fruit does not split open when it is ripe, but drops as a whole and is blown by the wind like a tumbleweed, until the capsule walls break down.

The single seed is a small globe, light brown and with a small keel,

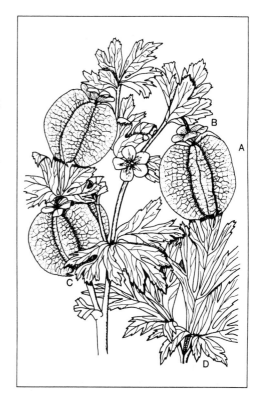

Helleborus vesicarius. A = fruiting stem with several inflated capsules, B = remains of flower, C = remains of styles, D = radical leaf (adapted from Mathew, *The Plantsman* 8, 3, 1986).

about the size of a mustard seed and lacking an elaiosome. Each year the stems die off in early summer and the plant remains dormant below ground during the hot summer. With the beginning of the winter rains, new stems grow and develop their flowers during the winter. Some sheaths appear first and are followed by basal leaves and a leafy stem. Both the basal and cauline leaves are divided into three parts, which are themselves very much dissected, like *Aconitum* leaves. The cauline leaves look similar to the basal leaves. As there are no membranous bracts, the plant has no aggregate terminal bud for the inflorescence but, in the same manner as *Helleborus lividus*, the flower buds develop successively in the axils of the cauline leaves. A branched stem bears about ten flowers, smaller than but similar to those of *H. foetidus*.

This plant does not seem to have much value for the average garden. It is probably best cultivated in a greenhouse and will be treasured by the enthusiast on account of its exotic fruits.

ORIGIN OF GARDEN FORMS AND HYBRIDIZATION

Natural Hybrids and Selected Forms

All hellebores have 32 chromosomes, which makes it possible for them to interbreed, though this is not common. Seedlings whose parents belong to different species, subspecies, forms or varieties are called hybrids. It is very unusual for hybrids to occur naturally between two species that are not members of the same genus, though artificial hybridizing techniques may be successful. All descendants of hybrids are themselves hybrids. The male parent contributes the pollen, i.e. the male germ cell. The female parent carries the female germ cell, or egg, in the ovary.

Such hybrids may occur spontaneously in the wild when two different forms of one species, or two subspecies of one species, or two different species of one genus, grow close together so that pollen from the male parent is easily transferred by insects to the stigma of the female parent. The results of such pollinations are known as natural hybrids. They do not occur very often, but can occasionally arise.

'Intermedius'

Schiffner considered it possible that the mysterious hellebore 'Intermedius' could be a natural hybrid between the closely related *Helleborus dumetorum* and *H. atrorubens*. It is very difficult to prove that such hybridization has taken place because no-one observes it happening. Only the results are seen, long afterwards, and the cross cannot be reproduced with certainty. In the meantime, the hybrid has spread and perhaps no obvious connection with the parents still exists. Sometimes, though, there is still a small population in the area inhabited by the parent species. With the help of chromosome comparisons and test crossings using the presumed species, it may be possible to determine the parentage of the hybrid.

Brian Mathew considers 'Intermedius' to be a variant of *Helleborus torquatus*. According to Ulbrich this plant, which is very rare even in its homeland, is a true species, and Margery Fish thought it to be identical with 'Torquatus'. The latter seems impossible as in the garden these two plants not only look different but behave differently.

The leaves of 'Intermedius' die off early, sprout again in March and are completely adult in April. The flower stem appears in February and remains in bud for a long time, looking similar to a flower stem of *Helleborus multifidus* of the same age. The narrow bracts and also the pea-sized buds are tinged with maroon. It differs from 'Torquatus' in its lighter, smaller leaves and in being a more refined, less robustly vigorous plant. From the appearance of the flower as well as that of the leaves, I consider 'Intermedius' to be

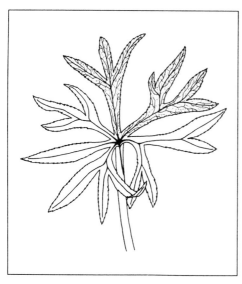

***Helleborus* 'Intermedius'. Radical leaf, natural size 19 × 14 cm (7½ × 5¼ in). The leaf has relatively slender divisions and is reddish-green at first. In style it resembles *Helleborus* 'Torquatus' and *H. multifidus*. Fine veining and marginal serrations. The basic form of the leaves is palmate.**

close to *H. multifidus*. Its distribution in northern Yugoslavia along with *H. atrorubens* and *H. dumetorum* does not necessarily mean that it is a hybrid between these two species. *Helleborus multifidus* is widespread and also occurs in these regions.

'Intermedius' flowers rather late. The short stem, which carries few flowers, has narrow cauline leaves and is rather similar to that of *Helleborus multifidus*. *Helleborus atrorubens* and *H. dumetorum* have multi-flowered inflorescences. The shape of the flower could equally be said to be similar to that of *H. multifidus*. In my opinion 'Intermedius' could just as easily be a hybrid of *H. multifidus* and *H. atrorubens* as of the two species suggested above. This would account for the finely serrated leaves and the lighter flower colour, a distinctive blend of yellowish green and red, and its reluctance to set seed.

The flower stem is only 20 cm (8 in) tall and divides into two branches low down, in the axil of a sheath. The branches are equal in length and one bears three flowers, the other only one. At the base of the flower stem there is a new radical leaf. The cauline leaves are small, with acuminate apexes to the lobes and reddish veins. The radical leaves have fewer leaflets than those of *Helleborus multifidus*. The leaflets of the young, still furled, new leaves are reddish beneath for half their length. The fully developed blade is held almost horizontal, on a slender petiole.

I think this plant needs warmth and is rather demanding. It dies back earlier than *Helleborus multifidus*, whereas in mild winters *H. dumetorum* may stay green. In any case, I believe that this plant, which as far as I can remember came from the Royal Horticultural Society's Garden at Wisley, is not identical with my 'Torquatus', which I received from Helen Ballard. Equally, I cannot see any similarity to *Helleborus dumetorum*, but a parentage involving *H. atrorubens* does seem possible because of its neat habit.

Specimens brought back by collectors are almost always selected forms. As the gene pool of a species nearly always contains a number of different genes for any particular character, there is usually some degree of variation among individuals of that species. Collectors search for the plants they consider the most beautiful and bring them home. If other people like it, the plant may be widely distributed as soon as circumstances permit. But if its rate of increase is slow, it will only spread into the hands of experts. That is what happened with 'Torquatus', for example, which was selected from many less beautiful representatives of the species. That was in 1928, and even today it is still very difficult to obtain.

'Torquatus'

'Torquatus' is a natural form of *Helleborus torquatus* (formerly *H. multifidus* subsp. *serbicus*). The plant has beautiful leaves, which are dull green on the upper surface, and its leaflets form a funnel. The old leaves die round about January and new young leaves appear in April, towards the end of the flowering season. New flower stems start to grow in February but flowering does not actually begin until about the end of March or beginning of April. The young flower heads are suffused with deep red but the radical leaves soon lose this colouring. The hairs on the undersides of the leaves also disappear quickly, but are in any case only scantily produced. 'Torquatus' is a charming, dainty plant in its early flowering stage, in spite of the single flower, which is on a long pedicel, being only medium-sized and drooping. It is a beautiful blackish-red, enhanced by a bluish bloom. Later on, when the radical leaves are mature, the plant is of medium size and fairly vigorous.

The cauline leaves, two beneath each flower, consist of very narrow segments. In the flowering season they are only 5 mm ($\frac{1}{4}$ in) wide, whereas the radical leaves have seven to eight leaflets, which are again divided into lobes slightly less than 1 cm ($\frac{3}{8}$ in) in width. At the base of the tepals, just below the rings of stamens, the flower has a white or slightly greenish zone, the 'torque' or collar that distinguishes this species and caused Archer-Hind, at that time

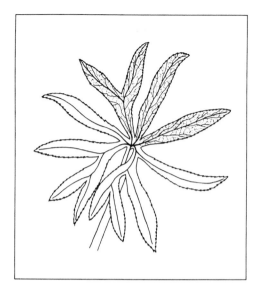

Helleborus 'Torquatus'. Selected form of *H. torquatus*. Radical leaf, natural size 25 × 25 cm (10 × 10 in). The young leaves are dark red at first, later becoming mid-green. The veins are not very conspicuous. The new leaves start into growth late.

a well-known hellebore collector, to give it the name 'Torquatus'. It has twice been found in its native habitat, on the last occasion by Ingwersen in 1978 near Peć in southern Yugoslavia.

This beautiful hellebore increases rather slowly in cultivation, but it has considerable horticultural value and is well worth searching for.

There are also natural double-flowered forms of *Helleborus torquatus*, found by Elizabeth Strangman and named 'Dido' and 'Aeneas'. In another version of their discovery, they are said to be seedlings of garden origin, from a double-flowered plant found some time previously.

Hybrids of Garden Origin

The third possible way by which garden forms may be produced is artificial hybridization. Species of a genus that would never normally come into contact with each other, for instance *Helleborus purpurascens* and *H. orientalis*, can be cross-fertilized. In this way it is even possible to produce fully fertile cultivars if the genetic differences between the parent species are not too great. This happens very often with hellebores but sometimes plants are created, especially by intersectional crosses, that are unable to set seed or do so only very reluctantly. An example of this is *H. × nigercors*, a hybrid between the species *H. niger* and the species *H. argutifolius.*

The majority of Lenten Roses, which originated through hybridizing among the species with radical leaves (with the exception of *Helleborus niger*), will propagate fairly readily from seed. Their descendants, however, are not identical with the parents even when the female parent has been self-pollinated. In this way gardeners have produced the most beautiful and decorative garden plants whose splendour and vitality often outshines that of the more modest species. But the hybridizer hoping for good results must bear in mind that no-one can breed any character from two parents that they did not originally possess. Hybridization simply combines formerly separate characters and

intensifies them through selection. It is a pity that insects all too often spoil the human hybridizer's plans, being so much better suited for the job. One has to resort to stratagems to foil them.

The species, forms and cultivars that flower during the hardest part of the year, such as *Helleborus niger* 'Praecox', *H.* 'Atrorubens', *H.* 'Galathé', and the earliest Lenten Roses, rarely set seed and have

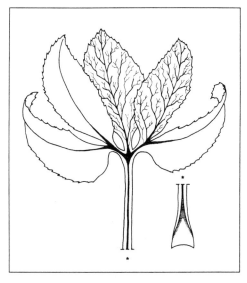

Helleborus × nigercors. Leaf from the lower part of the stem, natural size 27 × 20 cm (10¾ × 8 in). The overall shape of the leaf points to *H. niger*, the shape and colour of the leaflets bring to mind *H. argutifolius*. The tripartite division of the leaves of *H. argutifolius* is also still distinctly recognizable. The petiole is about 27 cm (10¾ in) long.

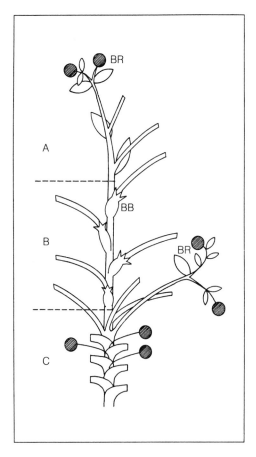

Diagram of flowering stem of Helleborus × nigercors. A = terminal part of inflorescence. Each branch has 2 or 3 flowers and is about 12 cm (4¾ in) long. B = middle part of inflorescence; it has about 4 branches in the axils of bracts with green, reduced blades; they are about 17 cm (6¾ in) long and carry three to four flowers. BR = greenish, soft bract without blade. BB = bract with reduced, greenish blade. C = lower part of stem; it bears at the top four branches, with two flowers; the lowest part carries the large stem leaves with, still, a pair of straggling flowers in the axils.

therefore been suspected of being sterile. They are best brought indoors for the purpose of hybridizing, being lifted on a sunny day when the soil is open. They should, of course, be already in bud. Plant in large pots and keep in a frost-free place, with as much light as possible. With proper care they grow on and flower as if nothing had happened.

It must not be forgotten that all hellebores are protogynous and self-fertile, which means that the stigmas are ripe very early, in fact as soon as the flower opens. So, shortly before the flower of the female parent opens naturally, the upper parts of the tepals and the anthers must be cut off with a small pair of scissors. By observing the tiny stigmas closely it is possible to see when their surfaces change, becoming rougher, at which point they are ripe. The anthers of the same flower, however, are still closed at that time and by removing them one can ensure that the only pollen reaching the stigmas is the desired one.

If the male (pollen) parent is growing outside in the garden, one of its flowers must be cut as soon as it opens, put in a glass of water and placed under a lamp. The upper tepals and, in this case, the style, are cut off. In this way a little 'pollen brush' is produced and when the right time arrives the female (pod) parent can easily be pollinated. During the next few days this procedure can be repeated several times, using the same 'pollen brush'.

If, later in spring, pollination is

carried out in the garden, it may be better to remove everything except the style from the female parent.

It is, of course, important to label each pollinated flower using a water-resistant pen. For this purpose the flexible white plastic strips used for closing bags are very suitable. It is easy to write on them with a permanent marker; they can then be rolled around the pedicel in an unobtrusive spot. Later they can be used as labels for the pots of seeds.

If the stamens and nectaries have not been removed, they drop off about a week after pollination; only the tepals and carpels remain. They turn green and provide an additional means of photosynthesis. Soon the carpels begin to swell. Unfortunately this is not a sure indication that pollination has been successful and seeds are developing. Sometimes the carpels are empty balloons, something quite often found with the hybrids that may be reluctant to set seed. But after a certain time has passed since the pollination was done, it is possible to feel the seeds inside the carpels and then it is necessary to look after the plant and see that it gets everything it needs for good development, especially sufficient light. It is probably best to plant it out in the garden again soon after the last frost, as seeds are not produced if the plant becomes drawn and lanky due to insufficient light. In a cold greenhouse, of course, this is not a problem.

Helleborus × *nigercors* **Wall.**

The hybrid *Helleborus* × *nigercors* resembles *H. argutifolius*, the Corsican Hellebore, in habit. That is, it has leafy stems not radical leaves, even though the lowest ones appear to emerge from the ground. The leaf blade is very large, divided into three parts, with a rough surface and sharply serrated edges. In autumn it is an attractive glossy green, but in the course of winter it becomes grey-green with whitish veins. At the upper end of the stem about 25 flowers develop that are as large as those of *H. niger*. They are very pale greenish creamy-white and grow in the axils of non-membranous, undivided green bracts such as are found on the Corsican Hellebore. The large head of white flower buds, which like those of *H. niger* are unprotected by bracts, is very showy. In late winter the buds slowly open one after another. The fully developed inflorescence is a marvellous sight. Each inflorescence is built up of a main stem with several side branches, each bearing several flowers. It is also possible to find specimens that tend more towards *H. niger* in form and leaf shape, which shows that this cross has been done several times with differing results. The first *H.* × *nigercors* was bred by a Mr Stooke. Elizabeth Strangman named one of her plants, probably the loveliest, 'Alabaster', and the plant described above is a sibling to 'Alabaster'.

As well as *Helleborus* × *nigercors*, there are in existence in England, if nowhere else, several examples of another cross, namely (*H. lividus* × *H. argutifolius*) × *H. niger*, or the reverse. In the *Bulletin* of the Hardy Plant Society for 1970, Eric Smith described making this cross and mentioned that it was successful. He subsequently named the resulting plants *H.* × *nigristern*.

A Hybrid raised by Helen Ballard

A hybrid between *Helleborus niger* and *H. lividus* was produced by Helen Ballard. My plant, a division planted three years ago in its present position, is still rather small. It has a 10 cm (4 in) tall brownish-red stem with three to four leaves similar in shape to those of *H. niger*, but smaller. They are a dull dark green in colour. The petiole is dark reddish-brown throughout its length. The inflorescence on this little plant has two side branches and carries 10 flowers. This hybrid hellebore flowers in January, the same time as *H. niger* subsp. *macranthus*. The relatively small flowers are white outside and green within, have glossy yellow-green nectaries and greenish styles and stamens. The flower grows from the axil of a bract about the size and shape of a fingernail. These bracts are very pale green and often have two teeth at the apex, probably the last remnant of a reduced blade.

After a very long and cold winter in 1986/87 this plant flowered at the end of April. The stem leaves withered at the start of the flowering season but this is obviously not normal, as the same plant retained its leaves when grown in a pot in England. In northern Germany this plant seems to be hardy, but in England in a cold part of Shropshire it does not flower unless kept in a cold greenhouse. It might be a good plant for an alpine garden but probably needs plenty of moisture. The new stems appear in April. To

Helleborus (H. niger × H. lividus). Stem leaf, natural size 24 × 21 cm (9½ × 8¼ in). As far as can be ascertained from the plant observed, it has inherited the majority of its characters from *H. niger*, apart from having more flowers per stem. The stem bears dark green leaves with leathery substance, shaped like those of *H. niger*, but not glossy. The base of the leaflets is very dark red and the petiole too is strongly flecked red.

date this plant has set no seed. It is probably sterile or at least not very willing to set seed, like *Helleborus × nigercors*, as in both cases the plants are interspecific hybrids. It is also similar to *H. × nigercors* in that it is prone to fungal disease. I am told that this was the hardiest plant resulting from the cross. Most of the seedlings tended towards *Helleborus lividus* and were grown by Helen Ballard in a cold greenhouse.

Helleborus × *sternii* **Turrill**

This is another hybrid of garden origin, named after its first raiser. Since then several people have repeated the cross and there are a number of forms of this hybrid. The aim of the hybridizer is to bring the pretty pink colouring on the reverse of the leaves and flowers in the best forms of *Helleborus lividus*, which are called 'Pictus', into the hybrids between *H. lividus* and *H. argutifolius*.

In shape the plants are close to the Corsican Hellebore, but somewhat shorter. The leaves, to some extent, show the veining present in *H. lividus* and, as has been said, the pink underside colouring of that species. As these plants are fertile, there are many different clones of the F_2 generation, which are sometimes more beautiful than the F_1 generation and on occasion produce surprising combinations. One such example is 'Wintersilber'.

'Wintersilber'

This appeared in a batch of F_2 seedlings. It is silvery green, without the red reverse to leaves and petals but with the very early flowering season of *Helleborus lividus*, which begins as early as August and lasts until May.

The flowering stem develops slowly and looks similar to that of *Helleborus argutifolius*, but the first flowers open when the main and side branches are just beginning to grow, i.e. at the end of August. Gradually the flower stem becomes as tall as that of *H. argutifolius*. 'Wintersilber' is like *H. lividus* in the way in which the inflorescence develops, but the final form of the flower-head is that of *H. argutifolius*.

All these hybrids, with their handsome flower-heads, remain attractive until the end of May, just before the seeds are ripe. In spite of the fact that the stems are still green and in good condition at that time, it is best to cut them off just above ground level before the garden becomes overcrowded with their seedlings, as can happen with hellebores. The new stems will then look all the better, shining in youthful splendour and, as yet, without flower buds.

These hellebores are green and attractive at all times of year, as long as they are not damaged by frost. In this respect they are very nearly comparable with dwarf conifers.

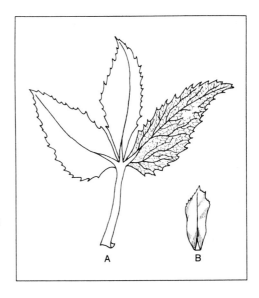

Helleborus × sternii F_2 **'Wintersilber'. A = stem leaf, natural size 25 × 18 cm (10 × 7 in); B = bract. The upper side of the stem leaves is, in common with the petiole, dark grey-green with light green veins. It is overlaid with a light bluish bloom when mature. The underside of the leaves is light grey-green. At the beginning of winter the leaf is silvery grey-green. The veining is finer and denser than in *H. lividus*. The scale-like bracts are whitish at the base, otherwise green like the leaf blades, not membranous.**

'Atrorubens'

At this point it is essential to discuss *Helleborus* 'Atrorubens' ('Early Purple') although (or simply because) no-one knows whether it is a natural form i.e. a natural hybrid, or one of garden origin. Everyone knows the 'Red Christmas Rose', everyone likes it, and very many keen gardeners grow it together with *H. niger* 'Praecox' in their gardens.

If one takes the trouble to look at it very closely, one can find characters from *Helleborus purpurascens* as well as from *H. atrorubens* and also *H. orientalis*, though the latter are less obvious. In cold winters the leaves die off earlier than those of *H. orientalis* but later than those of *H. purpurascens*. Its leaves are similar in nature to those of the Balkan species, but there is no known species in the wild that resembles 'Atrorubens'.

'Atrorubens' can be propagated by seed, which is set easily and in abundance after self- or foreign pollination, if the weather gives it the chance. As it may already be in flower in November, and also at any time during the winter whenever it is warm enough, it can easily be in flower when the temperature becomes unsuitable for successful pollination. It prefers a comfortable warmth of 2–4°C (35–40°F) like *Helleborus niger*. Its seedlings all look very much alike. There is a certain narrow diversity of characters but this remains within limits, as is usual with the species too; the leaves vary hardly at all. All the seedlings show a greater or lesser amount of white to green in their flowers. This is in the margins of the tepals which, because of this degree of white colouring, become increasingly washed out with age. The margins eventually become green. An example of a small difference was found in one seedling from 'Atrorubens', named 'Picoté': the individual flowers are poised at a different angle in that they are held firmly facing sideways.

The old leaves wither during the flowering period, which means the plant is semi-evergreen. The new leaves develop after the tepals have turned green, but in one of the 'Atrorubens' seedlings they grow at the same time as the flower stems and become adult very quickly. In hard winters 'Atrorubens' does not set seed in the open, though the flowers are open and the pollen even matures during mild spells.

I grew a plant of 'Atrorubens' indoors until it had set seed and what follows is a detailed description I drew up. At the time of the observation it was still at peak bloom and the first flowers had set seed. The new leaves were tightly wrapped in erect acute greenish-red sheaths and stood about 2 cm ($\frac{3}{4}$ in) above the surface of the soil.

One large radical leaf grows with each flower stem. In addition, the plant has large or slightly smaller radical leaves that seem to grow from rhizome branches not yet mature enough to flower. Radical leaves and flower stems are almost equal in height, the flower stems being only a little longer, but in mild winters they grow longer than this. The old radical leaves are beginning to go brown around their edges. In very hard winters they are dry and papery at flowering time. The leaflets are thin, but quite firm, and are finely and sharply toothed for more than three-quarters of their length from apex to base. The median leaflet is free and not dissected into lobes from the apex; the next two each have two lobes and the last two have three lobes each. As a whole, the blade appears almost palmate. It is 30 cm (12 in) in diameter, equal to the length of the petiole. The latter is somewhat canaliculate and angular, not fleshy. At the base it has a little brownish-red spotting. The blade is faintly glossy on both sides. The veins are narrow and only the central one is slightly raised.

Helleborus **'Atrorubens', the so-called 'Red Christmas Rose' ('Early Purple'). Its leaves wither in hard winters, in mild years it remains winter-green. Natural size of the leaves 30 × 25 cm (12 × 10 in).**

The inflorescence has two or three branches and is about 30 cm ($11\frac{3}{4}$ in) in height. Its base is rather thick and fleshy, with dark purple-brown hatching for half its length. This colour gradually disappears in the upper parts, where the stem becomes more angular than lower down. The first branch usually diverges just under halfway up the stem and is about as long as the main stem. Together they make a 45° angle. The second branch appears at a height of 25 cm (10 in) and, like the first one, rises from the axil of a five-partite herbaceous cauline leaf, which has a sheathing petiole. It may also be smaller or even scale-like. The second branch is opposite the first and is longer than the terminal of the main stem, which bears another, tripartite bract immediately above the second fork. A flower and a bud enclosed in two single-piece bracts grow in this axil. At the apex of each of the two side branches are two small tripartite bracts, one closely following the other. There is a bud in the axil of the first bract and a flower in the second. In total the inflorescence has six flowers and three buds.

Not all of the buds will develop. Whether a bud grows into a flower depends on the environmental conditions. A healthy plant has, on average, four to seven flowers in an inflorescence. The flowers are nodding, but after pollination they face upwards, raised by the contraction of the wrinkled skin beneath the flower.

When young the flowers are deep purple in colour, but later they become pale, especially on the inside, by developing their characteristic degree of white colouring, which gradually turns to green. The three to six carpels become darker as their veins turn purple, and the veins of the tepals also become darker as they age. It appears that the red pigment becomes concentrated in the veins.

A single flower has a diameter of 5–5.5 cm (2–2⅛ in). The five tepals are broad-ovate, about 2.5 cm (1 in) wide and 3.5–4 cm (1⅜–1⅝ in) long. Sometimes, just below the flower, a leaflet can be seen that is intermediate between a tepal and a bract, reddish green and toothed, like that described under *Helleborus purpurascens*.

The twelve nectaries are yellow-green, pressed together from above and almost closed by their incurved lips. The opening of the lips seems to be controlled by temperature.

The ovaries are barely as long as the nectaries, which are about twice as broad. The 30 stamens are a little shorter than the styles and, until they are ripe, cluster closely around the styles. As they ripen, the white filaments bend outwards. The anthers are small, about 1 mm × 2 mm ($\frac{1}{24} \times \frac{1}{12}$ in), and are cream-coloured, like the pollen.

At first the styles are light green and rather straight, even bending slightly outward. Later on they become brownish-violet. As the flowers age this colour appears also on the swelling ovaries and it is very noticeable that the styles bend first inward and then down, so far and so strongly that their tips finally protrude on the outside. There does not seem to be any description of this occurrence. Perhaps it only happens when the plant is grown under cover?

The carpels have a very short 'stem' and are keeled, the keel running the full length of the outer side and halfway down the inner side.

Work on the Genus up to the Present Day

From 1853 Alexander Braun collected the southern European and near-Eastern species of the genus *Helleborus* in order to study them in the garden of the University of Berlin and the Botanical Garden of Berlin-Schöneberg. He wrote up his observations in *Index Seminum Hort. Bot. Berol.* 1861 and in doing this he produced an essential work on the distribution of these plants and information about the genus in Europe.

In 1858, in the *Berliner Allgemeine Gartenzeitung*, Karl Koch described those species he himself had collected in 1857. His great merit lies in the accuracy of his descriptions. This is why Viktor Schiffner gave his name to the plant he regarded as the central form of the *Helleborus orientalis* group: *Helleborus kochii*. After these two works an increasing amount was published in the nineteenth century, especially in the 1880s.

Probably the earliest hybrids involving *Helleborus orientalis, H. guttatus, H. abchasicus, H. kochii* and *H. olympicus* (for current names see the species descriptions) were grown in the Berlin Botanical Garden between 1853 and 1880. Many, particularly the dark forms, came from the German plant enthusiast Max Leichtlin. Otto Fröbel, in Switzerland, was also hybridizing in his nursery, working to produce beautiful cultivars. The Heinemann nursery in Erfurt sold hybrids raised by the amateur breeder Professor Schleicher and probably produced some new cultivars of its own; in any case, it named some.

When people in England began to take an interest in hellebores, many German cultivars appeared in the lists of the better-known nurseries. The first English breeders were Sir Frederick Stern with the famous *Helleborus × sternii* and Thomas Archer-Hind, who produced, among others, the pretty 'Primrose Dame'. The then very famous 'Black Knight' is said to have come from Europe, probably from Max Leichtlin.

The old hybridizers, with the exception of Alexander Braun and his gardener Sauer, have left no records to show how they obtained their sometimes splendid cultivars. Many of today's colours were already in existence then, but almost all of them have vanished; almost none are still listed by nurseries except for 'Black Knight'. That is a warning for the future, for if the parentage of these plants had been recorded, we could at least try to repeat the crosses.

Up to 1989, the most comprehensive monograph on the genus was that written by Viktor Schiffner in 1891. He showed the relationships between its members in a manner that makes them very easy to see, and his monograph is still highly regarded in most respects. However, he named five species now grouped together under *Helleborus orientalis*. After Schiffner several botanists dealt with the genus in floras published since then; the treatment of the genus has in the main been based on Schiffner's classification.

In 1908 E. Ulbrich became the successor to Alexander Braun, so to speak, when he prepared a species index with synonyms for the reorganization of the botanical collections in Berlin-Dahlem. This was also the basis of his later description *Die Arten der Gattung Helleborus (Tournefort) L.*, 1937. In this he generally relied on Schiffner's work, but he put up a new section for the East Asiatic species, namely Section V, *Dicarpon* Ulbrich. The hybrid forms *Helleborus* × *nigercors* Wall. (1934) and *H.* × *sternii* were obviously unknown to him, as he said that all hybrid forms should be put into Section VI, *Eubelleborus* Schiffner: 'The main swarm of the hybrids, which in general are hard to disentangle, falls into the species with beautifully coloured violet or purple, red or yellowish flowers ... obviously very soon after their introduction the species of central Europe have frequently been crossed with the southern European and Eastern ones.'

He therefore provided no revision of the hybrids known up to that time, as he would have needed many years of hybridizing trials using absolutely true species for such a revision. He reproduced the descriptions of the hybrids as Schiffner had given them.

Pareys Blumengärtnerei of 1958 was also still based on Schiffner's ideas and classification. As far as the European species were concerned, a change came in 1961 through Merxmüller and Podlech. Their work was published in Fedde's *Repetitorium* 64, 1–8. In *Flora of Turkey*, P.H. Davis and J. Cullen combined all the forms from Asia Minor under one species, *Helleborus orientalis*. Brian Mathew's little booklet, *A Gardener's Guide to Hellebores*, was again based on Schiffner's work.

G. Hegi, who also followed the taxonomy of Schiffner and Ulbrich, at last provided some new cytological information about the genus in his *Illustrierte Flora von Mitteleuropa*. He reported on Harvey's observations of meiotic processes in a human-made hybrid between *Helleborus argutifolius* and *H. foetidus*. He stated that both parents were allotetraploid species with the genotype formulae AABB and BBCC respectively. Of course he knew nothing of the other hybrids in existence today, those between *H. niger* and the Caulescentes or between two different species of the Caulescentes. He described the biology of the flower and the distribution very thoroughly.

When modern hybridizing started, it was the British who followed their predecessors Stern, Archer-Hind and others. First and foremost there is Helen Ballard, to date the most successful hybridizer not just in Britain, but in the world. Her aim is to breed intense, clean, light and dark colours. Any mixed with green or a pattern are usually discarded. She also selects large flowers that face sideways.

The next hybridizer who must be mentioned is Elizabeth Strangman. Her *Helleborus* × *nigercors* 'Alabaster' has already been cited, and the double forms 'Dido' and 'Aeneas' are famous. Eric Smith, well known in connection with other plants too, produced a number of beautifully spotted hellebores and primrose yellow ones. He named his spotted cultivars after the starry sky, 'Scorpio', 'Hercules', 'Sirius' and 'Cosmos'.

Helen Ballard lists a great many named cultivars. Some have upward- or side-facing flowers, like the primrose yellow 'Citron', blue 'Indigo', green 'Parrot' and 'Helen Ballard' and pink 'Upstart'. Others, as well as 'Indigo', have a metallic blue sheen: the tall graceful 'Blue Wisp' and the early, robust blue-black 'Philip Ballard'. There are different green cultivars, 'Parrot' being brilliant green, 'Helen Ballard' bright green, and 'Greencups' a true green. There are some spotted flowers, such as the deep purple 'Hecate', light red 'Dotty' and clear pink 'Philip Wilson'. As well as the pale yellow 'Citron' there is 'Ingot', to date the deepest yellow but extremely slow to increase. White is represented by three named forms: 'Sylvia', a delicate white, 'Ushba', well formed, a strong grower and absolutely pure white, and finally 'Button', a creamy white. Others include vigorous 'Rubens', which carries large deep red blooms, 'Dick Crandon' with its nodding, clear light pink bells, and 'Dusk', which shows the metallic blue caused by a bluish

bloom, on the inside of its flowers.

Newer cultivars Helen Ballard has released – hellebore breeders are known to be very reluctant to part with their children! – are 'Blue Spray', of medium size, bluish and graceful; 'Blowsy', with big, loosely formed creamy yellow flowers; 'Cheerful', similar to 'Citron' but not as lush; 'Dawn', a good large pink form; 'Garnet', brownish red; 'Hades', slate blue with darker spots; 'Lynne' which carries a profusion of white bowls, and is faintly spotted; 'Nocturne', dark, with small but almost true blue flowers; 'Patchwork'

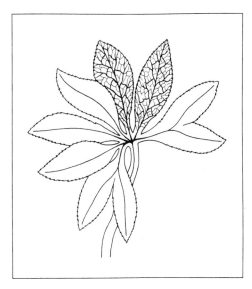

Helleborus 'Citron'. Radical leaf, natural size 28 × 25 cm (11 × 10 in). The leaf of this yellow-flowered hybrid withers during the winter. This suggests a cross involving a species that is, at least sometimes, winter-bare. In this case it would seem to be H. odorus.

with small flowers in green and light blue; 'Rembrandt', darkish brown-red with dark young leaves and stems; 'Rosa', rose-red; 'Rossini' with upright clear red flowers; and 'Sunny', creamy yellow, well formed and full of vitality.

Helen Ballard's current goals, she told me, are to breed plants with apricot-coloured and medium blue flowers. May the goddess Flora grant her a long life!

Double-flowered Lenten Roses have been bred by Günther Jürgl at Sürth, near Köln in Germany. One of these is white, the other is finely spotted pink on a white ground so that it appears pink.

In Germany, the breeder Heinz Klose at Kassel-Lohfelden could be called the successor to all these older and more recent breeders. He started by collecting every plant he could find, and then worked with them for 10 or 12 years. Thousands of seedlings bear witness to his work. What has so far emerged deserves to be called very remarkable. The most striking are his spotted cultivars such as the light pink, spotted light red, 'Frühlingsschale'. His powder-blue with blue-black spots, 'Nachthimmel', is astonishing, as are also the red-black, mysterious forms 'Gewitternacht' and 'Schwarzes Gold', which are thrillingly beautiful but not at all strident or harsh. Many more wonderful flowers are still in his greenhouses, for instance seedlings from crosses between the double Jürgl plants and 'Dido' and 'Aeneas'. These of course still have to prove

themselves as garden plants.

In the future, many plants that as yet have only flowered in the privacy of their breeders' homes will enrich the gardens of hellebore-lovers. As Margery Fish wrote: 'We shall all envy the owners of gardens with enough shade to grow all the hellebores they want.' They will be as happy during the winter as other people are in spring and summer, filled with hope, excitement and delight. But it must be added that these fantastic Lenten Roses are, as it were, only just born. The hybridizer rejoices in their existence and hopes, with luck, to propagate them. What a wonderful prospect!

In the spring of 1989 the latest scientific work on the genus was published as *Hellebores* by Brian Mathew. His classification is used in this book:

Genus *Helleborus* Linn.
Section I. Syncarpus
    1. *Helleborus vesicarius*
Section II. Griphopus
    2. *Helleborus foetidus*
Section III. Chenopus
    3. *Helleborus argutifolius*
    4. *Helleborus lividus*
Section IV. Helleborus
    5. *Helleborus niger*
Section V. Helleborastrum
    6. *Helleborus orientalis*
    7. *Helleborus cyclophyllus*
    8. *Helleborus purpurascens*
    9. *Helleborus torquatus*
    10. *Helleborus atrorubens*
    11. *Helleborus dumetorum*
    12. *Helleborus viridis*

13. *Helleborus odorus*
14. *Helleborus multifidus*
Section VI. Dicarpon
15. *Helleborus thibetanus*

The order in which the species are dealt with in this book is practically the reverse of Brian Mathew's. This expresses my ideas on the course of evolution in this genus, but I do not claim that they are scientifically proven.

Thoughts on Hybridizing

In *The Garden*, the Journal of the Royal Horticultural Society, for January 1987 an article by Helen Ballard appeared in which she described the steps by which she achieved hellebores with yellow flowers. With the exception of the article by Eric Smith on crossing *Helleborus niger*, *H. argutifolius* and *H. × sternii* already mentioned, this was the first report on modern hybridizing, at least as far as coloured hellebores are concerned. In her article Helen Ballard relates how she used *H. odorus* subsp. *laxus* Host, *H. olympicus* and white hybrids of *H. orientalis* to produce the cultivar 'Citron'. It is obvious that such records are immensely valuable, for if no written guidance is available hybridizers have to start at the beginning with their own experiments and detailed observations of plants and seedlings. In other words, a hybridizing goal must be defined, parents must be sought out, crosses made, seed sown, seedlings selected and sibling crosses made, and so on. And very painstaking record-keeping is essential. In a couple of years breeders can acquire an intensive knowledge of their plants. This can be demonstrated by a few simple examples.

A large sowing of seeds from a beautiful *Helleborus niger* subsp. *macranthus* with a rosy flush on the reverse of the tepals resulted in about 80 seedlings. Only two of these were pure white, all the rest being more or less flushed with pink. From this result it can be inferred that pink colour in *H. niger* subsp. *macranthus* is a dominant character, whilst its non-appearance is due to a recessive character. As there are different degrees of intensity of colour, this feature is probably controlled by several genes. Incidentally, it was observed that in a very cold early spring this pigment was only weakly expressed. Perhaps its formation is influenced by temperature.

If two of the white-flowered plants are crossed, it is almost certain that no pink-flushed flowers will be produced. But by cross- or self-pollinating the pink-flushed flowers, most of their descendants will have more or less pink-flushed blooms. As only pure white flowers are in demand for cut flowers at Christmas, this is an important point to remember.

The flowers of 'Frühlingsfreude', from Heinz Klose, are densely spotted and veined dark purple on a white ground. Another plant that came from Klose under the name of 'Brunhilde' (in the past there was a 'Brunhilde' of a different colour) has soft pink flowers, finely spotted. The two are planted side by side in my garden and flower at the same time. Some seeds collected from 'Frühlingsfreude' could only have resulted from self-pollination or a cross between these two plants. Nearly all the 24 seedlings had soft pink, dark pink or red flowers; one was yellow-green, two were white, and only two were of the dotted, veined type. From this it seems that the production of plain pink or red types is less complicated than producing the dotted, veined type, and also simpler than both yellow-green and white. The pink and red types are probably the expressions of one, or maybe two, anthocyanins but these are present in many degrees of intensity. The presence of the anthocyanin could follow the dominant/recessive pattern, but its intensity again seems to be controlled by specific genes, if this were not the case, the range would not be as wide as it is.

When yellow-green and white occur in a flower in pure form they are probably completely recessive, i.e. all four gene-loci in the tetraploid hellebore must be occupied by them for the colours white or yellow-green to be expressed. Or to put it the other way round: white crossed with white results in white, yellow-green crossed with yellow-green gives yellow-green again.

Naturally, these suggestions are not intended to be the last word on the inheritance of flower colour in hellebores. The topic is too complicated and the number of plants under observation too small. They are merely meant to encourage readers to make their own experiments and form their own conclusions. It could be a very absorbing occupation!

One can only guess at the origin of the phenotype of dotted and veined flowers. It must surely be controlled by many, possibly recessive, genes for pattern and colour, but one cannot even conjecture as to how they interact.

A bluish 'bloom' is very often involved in the colouring of hellebore flowers, mainly in the dark types. It darkens the red colour and makes it appear blue. It can be rubbed off and has, in fact, nothing to do with pigmentation. Observing its mode of inheritance is very difficult. When the tepals are thickly coated with this bloom, the flower is a wonderful powdery blue.

Some of the pink hellebores have a more or less orange tone, others have a cleaner old rose colour than the bulk of the seedlings. It seems likely that a greater or lesser amount of flavones is responsible for this phenomenon, or that the outer and inner layers of tissue in the tepals contain different pigments.

It is clear that there are not only genetic patterns that are expressed in manifold variations in the distribution of spotting, but patterns of colour distribution as well. The two outer tepals may, for instance, be darker than the three inner ones, or all may be darker on the outside, e.g. red, and lighter within, in this case pink. It is interesting to speculate on whether this colour distribution pattern could be obtained with other colours as well: would it be possible to get a flower that is white inside with blue-black on the outside, or yellow inside with blue outside? Thinking in this way is not at all unrealistic, one has only to look at the handsome form of *Helleborus purpurascens* with bright olive green inside and purple on the backs of the tepals that is available commercially in Britain. Separate zones of the tepals may have different colours. The base can be dark purple, the middle part red, the zone outside this whitish and the apex green, as can be seen in many seedlings from 'Atrorubens' ('Early Purple').

A very striking example of the way in which the patterns for flower marking and colour distribution can be combined together in a most surprising way and produce flowers of completely new aspect is Klose's 'Monika'. This flower makes it clear that there are certain areas in the hellebore flower that are capable of containing different pigments. After the anthers and nectaries have been shed, the flower remains beautiful for a while: in the centre is a circular white disc about 1 cm ($\frac{3}{8}$ in) in diameter, and around this is a light brown ring of about 3 cm ($1\frac{1}{8}$ in) diameter. Both are bordered by a wreath of dark rays consisting of the above-mentioned tiny red-brown dots, which in this flower are gathered around the central zone and along the veins to form the wreath or corona. The outer ends of the dark rays coincide with the end of the next ring of colour, which is deep pink, against which the rays show up very well. Outside this is yet another ring of very pale pink, which is sprinkled with very fine dots. The whole effect is surprisingly attractive. A pattern of this kind is sometimes called 'eyed'. The green/white/pink zones underlie the corona of rays.

Such flowers can lead to further daydreams. How about a yellow flower with a sharply accented black-purple corona? The combination of these individual characteristics has only become possible after several generations of hybridizers have taken the hellebores in hand, which means that they have mixed the species together very thoroughly and then selected good combinations of characters. The spots, and perhaps also the circular zones, may have come from *Helleborus guttatus*. The central white disc stems from *H. torquatus*, which passes it as a dominant character to its seedlings. The brown ring probably indicates the effect of the yellow-green *H. orientalis* (*H. kochii*).

Who knows what results are yet to come when other species, not yet used in hybridizing, are introduced into the cross-pollinations? But anyone who wants to hybridize hellebores should certainly not follow the old lines already well explored by Max Leichtlin and Alexander Braun and try, for example, to produce yet another deep black hellebore, beautiful though it may be. I am quite sure that hellebores have many more beautiful aspects that could be brought to light.

Helen Ballard has shown us that beauty can be found in quieter colours as well as bright ones, by naming three green-flowered hellebores. As she has watched the

**Leaf of a hybrid from *Helleborus*
'Torquatus', Natural size 27 × 21 cm
(10¾ × 8¼ in).**

coming and going of so many hybrid
seedlings in her garden, these three
must surely be so lovely and so
different from each other that she
could not resist giving them the
distinction of their own names. Since
so many delicate shades of green
already exist among the species, this
could be a rewarding field of work.
Green flowers are in great demand
by flower arrangers.

The nectaries, as well as the tepals,
can add extra colour to the flower.
Metallic blue-black or dark blackish-
red are emphasized by bright
greenish-yellow nectaries. Red-brown
nectaries give a porcelain pink flower
still greater charm, and brown
nectaries enhance a yellow bloom.

So far no hybridizer has
concentrated on hellebore leaves, but

they are very good foliage plants.
Combining the profusion of finely-cut
leaflets borne by some forms of
Helleborus multifidus with interesting
flower colours and shapes would be
a very worthwhile project. If they
carried smaller but more abundant
flowers these plants could be graceful
assets for shady places.

Finally, there is one hybridizing
goal to be suggested which would be
welcomed especially by keen
gardeners. It would be wonderful if
someone could create plants with the
beautiful flowers of modern hybrids
but which produced their new
growth later in spring and remained
green all summer. A lot of problems
with winter protection would then be
avoided.

There are, of course, many
possible further developments that
we cannot begin to imagine. It is by
no means rare, in plant breeding, for
reality to overtake fantasy.

Cultivation And Use

Climatic conditions for hellebores in cultivation are often different from those in their natural environment. Above all it is the temperatures that cause problems.

The British Isles have an easy time as far as winter temperatures are concerned. The Gulf Stream exercises such a strong influence that roses and pampas grass can grow and flower in Scotland at a latitude of 58° North, and subtropical trees and other plants can flourish in the garden of Inverewe. In some parts of England winters can be Mediterranean in character, with temperatures no lower than 0°C (32°F) and more rain than snow.

In Europe, however, winter months are in some years very cold and dry. Minus 25°C (−13°F) is a temperature frequently recorded and one has to be prepared for this every winter. However, as in northern Germany the North Sea has a similar influence, the weather can change from one day to the next and become as mild as an 'all mud and slush' English winter. It

is best to have deep snow on the ground, as this provides warm shelter for the plants underneath it. In bad years there is biting frost with no snow cover, which damages them badly. In Spring there are the wide differences between quite hard frosts at night and warm sunshine during the day, which are dangerous to plants. This see-sawing between maritime and continental climates is the big disadvantage of the north German winter.

Summers can have warm dry spells, but can also resemble Mediterranean winters by being cool and wet. As can be seen, we demand a lot of these plants when we introduce them into our gardens. Fortunately hellebores have within themselves the ability to exist in these conditions as most of them inhabit hilly or mountainous regions where the temperature drops as the height increases, so they are adapted to changes in temperature, though not quite sufficiently to cope with severe winters.

Propagation by Seed and Division

Hellebores are perennials that prefer to grow in a favourable spot for a very long time. They do not like to be disturbed. The longer the plants are allowed to grow in the same spot, the more imposing and beautiful they become. In this respect they seem made for the gardens of intelligent but lazy gardeners.

It is a pity that hellebores must be disturbed when they are being propagated. Once again the Lenten Roses, the representatives of the *Helleborus orientalis* hybrids, are the ones that resent this operation the least. One digs them up carefully, shakes the soil from the roots, and divides the plant into as many crowns as possible. They recover better from this rigorous treatment than if several crowns are kept together.

They should be planted 50 cm (20 in) apart. Of course they should not be out of the ground for long, especially not when the sun is shining. A cloudy day is best for dividing them. The larger the single crown, the sooner it will start flowering again, possibly as early as the following spring. However, if dormant buds with a few roots are planted, which may sometimes be possible in favourable conditions, they will require the same time (two to four years) as a seedling does to grow to flowering size. This method should only be used for mass propagation of named cultivars or species. These divisions are best grown on in a greenhouse until they are large enough to be planted out, as losses may occur in the garden. From then on they can be handled in the same way as larger divisions.

Tissue culture of hellebores is just being started. The first cultivar, 'Ushba', and some unnamed seedlings have been successfully propagated for the first time, but are not widely available as yet. The genus has for a long time resisted this new technique, so it still has to prove its suitability.

It is better not to divide *Helleborus niger* into such small pieces as the Lenten Roses, because they will take a very long time to recover. A good compromise is for each division to comprise three crowns. They will usually flower again in the following spring. *Helleborus niger* 'Praecox' is particularly sensitive in this respect, but it is also this plant that shows, by its leaves turning yellow and its flowers diminishing in size, that it needs to be transplanted. When this happens, first try to delay the move for a year by giving a dressing of lime and trace elements. It seems that 'Praecox' exhausts the soil, especially a light soil, faster than other species. The only other one to do this is *H. cyclophyllus*. If this treatment does not help, then all the black, corky remains of the old rhizomes must be removed and the crowns, including the small ones, are replanted singly. The result, of course, is a large number of plants, but it will be two to three years before they flower again. *Helleborus niger*, like *H.*

cyclophyllus, needs a lot of lime, and it may be a lack of this that prevents it from thriving.

The only hellebores difficult to propagate by division are the stemmed ones, as their rhizomes are very short-jointed and also very woody, so that dividing them requires a lot of strength. In such cases, provided one is not dealing with named cultivars, which must be propagated vegetatively, propagation by seed is the better method. Even with the few named cultivars it is better to try self-pollination to get seedlings that come true. This does mean that one has to wait until they flower to see whether this has worked, but avoids the hard work of dividing the rhizomes. There is also the danger that the divided stem may not grow new roots.

For dividing the rhizomes, a large knife, or better still a saw or an axe, is necessary if the division is being made in late summer and stems with some roots attached are wanted. Clearly, it is hardly feasible to do this without lifting the whole plant, as nobody would want to endanger a precious *Helleborus* x *nigercors* or 'Wintersilber'. If a stem is cut off without roots, it will be six months before new ones start to grow. To date there is nobody with experience of detaching the newly-grown soft young stems in spring. Perhaps the problems could be avoided by treating them as cuttings, but this method of propagation can only be tried when sufficient plant material is available.

With the Balkan species and good cultivars it is best for the beginner to be very cautious, removing a single crown from the main plant with great care. This crown is subsequently used for further propagation, so that the original plant can remain undisturbed.

Although not every seedling is worth keeping (especially those from *Helleborus orientalis* hybrids) it is sometimes rewarding to propagate by seed, as long as one is strong-willed about discarding poor plants. If seed is not wanted it is best to break off the pollinated carpels as soon as possible, or to cut the whole flower stem when the last flowers have finished blooming, as seed production makes demands upon the strength of the plant. Another reason is that a ripe carpel on a hellebore splits open very easily and the following spring sees unwanted and worthless seedlings coming up in the centre of the parent plant. They distress and weaken the good cultivar or, even worse, supersede it. If that cultivar has to be divided, the seedlings may lead to confusion in naming.

The Acaulescent European species must probably be grown from seed as most of them are rarely offered by nurseries. Unfortunately it is just these plants that are most reluctant to germinate.

For successful propagation of hellebores from seed, correct timing is of enormous importance. Seed must be sown before it goes dormant, which it does very quickly once it is dry. On the other hand, it is obviously impossible to prevent the seed going dormant by keeping it moist in a plastic bag as it will grow moulds when kept over winter.

The seed must therefore be gathered as early as possible, that is as soon as the carpels become yellowish-green and can be opened by gently squeezing them with the fingers. At this time the seeds are glossy black, except for those of *Helleborus vesicarius*. It is advisable not to wait until the capsules open naturally, as ants will carry off at least some of the seeds for the sake of the elaiosome.

It is best to sow the seed as soon as it is harvested, using deep clay pots half filled with soil. If the garden soil in which the adult plants are growing is not too coarse, it is not necessary to add extra seed compost. Light does not affect the germination of hellebore seeds, so they can be placed on top of the soil, which makes it very easy to keep them under observation. The deepest possible pots are the best to choose, because the seedlings very quickly develop rather long roots.

The clay pots are then plunged in a shady spot, with the rim of the pot above the soil surface. In dry weather, care must be taken to see that they do not dry out, but apart from that they can be left to the mercies of the weather. As soon as leaves start to fall from the trees, they should be used to cover the pots, and it is wise to put some slug poison around, too.

The seeds start to germinate from early November. This can easily be supervised by looking under the leaf cover. The tiny white root tip is very conspicuous when it starts to penetrate the seed coat. At this point it is very important to keep the seeds moist. They should now be moved close to the house, or into the house or greenhouse if they are to be overwintered under cover. It is possible to grow them on it a light and frost-free place but they can equally well stay in the garden under the leaf covering, in which case the covering must be removed in good time in spring so that the seedlings do not become lanky and weakly. Birch or oak leaves seem to encourage germination, and in the house or greenhouse it is best to turn the leaves over or take them off for a while each day. The warmth and moisture underneath the leaves probably provide the right conditions, similar to those in nature. As soon as the root tips appear, cover the seeds with a thin layer of soil.

Even if the seedlings have no more than their first two seed leaves, they will not be killed by frost in the open. In one case, a large clay pot with about 50 such seedlings stood at first under a covering of snow, which melted. The water could not drain away, because the peat in which the pot was plunged stayed frozen, and neither could the pot be lifted out. The next night the water froze and for the next two weeks the seedlings had to live completely encased in clear ice. Then the ice thawed. Before spring arrived, this happened again, twice. In the end, these 'cotyledon-only' seedlings looked rather dishevelled and a few were dead, but the main mass were alive and grew on. It does seem that they are truly hardy.

The seedlings can be pricked out as soon as they are large enough to be handled, at the moment when the first true leaf has started to develop between the cotyledons. It seems that the little plants suffer much less from disturbance at this stage than they do later on, probably because the root is not yet long, branched, and vulnerable. Naturally it is still necessary to take care not to damage the root tip. If they are pricked out early, three seedlings can be put in one 10 cm (4 in) pot, though of course it is better to pot them up singly, in this case in a plastic pot to reduce transpiration. The plants should be planted out in the open garden after the middle of May.

At this time the seedlings that have been outside all winter are naturally not as advanced, but they will not usually have suffered from the winter weather. These too should be planted out in summer as soon as they are large enough. If they are planted straight into their final positions, it is essential to mark them with a large and conspicuous label that will not get trodden into the soil, especially those that lose their leaves in winter. Otherwise it is best to transplant them into a special bed and move them to their proper places in the following spring.

As a rule, the first plants to flower do so in their third year, 'Atrorubens' ('Early Purple') sometimes in its second, but most flower in their fourth year and some laggards wait until the fifth. Every plant should be allowed to flower twice before any selection is made, because the flowers often fail to show their full potential in their first blooms.

Helleborus foetidus, H. lividus, H. argutifolius and *H. niger* should always be propagated by seed. When the plants are already in the garden, it is worthwhile letting them seed naturally. If there are too many seedlings they are easily removed with the hoe, but sometimes good forms can be picked out. Often the seedlings, especially those of *H. foetidus*, find themselves quiet corners which they decorate perfectly.

As has already been said, naturalizing is not to be recommended for the special hybrid Lenten Roses, but of course one can sow the seeds resulting from hand pollination under the parent plant, as long as a careful watch is kept on them. It is said that germination is excellent and problem-free in this spot, and this seems to be correct. The reason probably is that seed that has fallen under the pod parent has, quite literally, been sown the moment it is ripe. But seedlings growing in such a spot must be transplanted as soon as possible, as the adult plant will kill them by depriving them of light, water and nourishment.

Hellebore seeds, as has been mentioned, remain viable for only a very short time. If they have gone dormant, they will germinate during the following season but the germination rate will not be the full 100 per cent, whilst in the winter immediately after ripening, before they go dormant, 100 per cent germination can be expected. Some dormant seeds will even wait until the following season. This is Nature's wise precaution to ensure that a species will survive even if germination conditions in any one year are bad. Many of the seeds seem to lose viability completely. The seed of *Helleborus vesicarius* is said to remain viable for five years, which must surely be advantageous in its home country, but this does not happen in our climate.

Planting and General Care

New roots begin to grow in March, or in April with the later species. They are white and easily broken off. If hellebores are to be transplanted in spring, it is therefore recommended that this should be done as early as possible, i.e. during the flowering period when root growth has not yet stopped. If the plants are kept well watered, they scarcely seem to notice that they have been moved. This is probably the best time for the less hardy species and cultivars such as the *Helleborus niger* group and the Balkan species, and for valuable hybrids of the Lenten Roses, as the new roots enable them to grow on well. The stronger Lenten Roses can be transplanted at any time except when the soil is frozen, provided the operation is carried out with care.

With the stemmed species transplanting is not difficult in itself if the plant is still young, but large older plants do not take kindly to being moved. So it is better to make sure that there is always a succession of seedlings growing on before the older plants die. As they are said to be short-lived in some gardens, such foresight is to be recommended.

With the exception of a few early-flowering selections and hybrids, hellebores start to develop their flowerbuds and inflorescence buds about the beginning of October. The flowers open between January and May except for, again, the precocious forms such as 'Atrorubens' ('Early Purple'), 'Galathé' and *Helleborus*

niger 'Praecox'. The old leaves die off before, during or after flowering, depending on the species. Depending on the time of flowering, the seeds ripen between May and August. In the period between seed ripening and the initiation of flower development in October, the plant starts to grow new crown buds underground. At this time of year the roots are blackish-brown and rubbery but are nevertheless still functioning.

This is another time of year favourable for transplanting. If the late summer period is hot and dry, it is essential to give sufficient watering, but if as so often happens the transition from summer to autumn is a gentle one with cool, rainy days, the hellebores can be left to look after themselves.

As can be seen from their growth cycle, hellebores need plenty of water, especially in the first half of the year, and this should be given as evenly as possible. In summer, after their seed is ripe, they can stand more warmth and drier conditions. During the winter months they need moisture too, because that is when the buds are growing, but as they cannot take up frozen water, growth will be suspended until better weather arrives.

Hellebores are not particular as far as soils are concerned. It is often said that *Helleborus niger* and its hybrids need heavy, moisture-retentive soils, but on the other hand they, like all hellebores, need efficient drainage. Light soils can be changed to suit them by adding clay and humus where they are to be planted. Heavy soils can, conversely, be improved by adding sand and leaf-mould, as waterlogging must be avoided since neither *H. niger* nor any of the other hellebores will tolerate it. Any soil that is not alkaline should have some lime added to it, as hellebores do not do well without lime. Some old mortar rubble dug into the soil is quite sufficient for this purpose.

All hellebores need a soil that is well-aerated, something best done by earthworms, as is well known. This is especially true of the soil close to the plants as they resent hoeing, digging and so on among their roots. The natural leaf fall from trees and shrubs should, therefore, be allowed to stay where it is, and where there is none, a good depth of mulch every year ensures that earthworms will find conditions to their liking and will increase in number. Plenty of well-rotted garden compost should be dug in first when any planting is done.

All in all, it can be said that with compost, clay, lime or chalk, trace elements if necessary, perhaps some sand in heavy soil, and a mulch of suitable material, the needs of the plants will be satisfied.

All need a deep planting hole so that the roots can be kept straight in the soil. Roots should not be bent nor cut off as, if other conditions are not right, this could lead to fungal infections. Very often the roots will branch if the tips have been cut off, thus creating new root tips.

With the exception of the *Helleborus orientalis* hybrids, the Lenten Roses, the requirements of the species as to the situations they prefer can be quite distinctive and the gardener really should give some time and thought to this. It should never be forgotten that these plants come from southern Europe, mostly around the Mediterranean Sea, and their most active period of growth comes in what is, in more northerly regions, the hardest part of the year.

A sheltered, warm (but even in summer, not too hot) place, without drying winds in winter, and in light shade, suits hellebores best. Lenten Roses like dappled shade all the time, not full shade for half the day and sun for the other half. The southern European hellebores, though, like more warmth in summer and can stand some sunshine, so a place should be found for these species that has shade in winter and spring, because of late frosts, but which will be sunnier in summer, so providing conditions that approximate to those of their native regions.

It is even better to avoid early morning and late evening sun falling on the plants in winter and spring, so that they are not exposed to marked differences in temperature. For all these reasons, the hellebore grower should look for places in the garden that have full shade in winter and spring only. There is naturally more shade available in winter than in summer.

Planting places should also not be too dry, which they can be under a balcony or the eaves of the house, or where there are roots of other plants.

Hellebores come from regions of winter rainfall where they normally receive plenty of water in the growing season. They will be hard done by in dry spots if they have to depend for water on a forgetful gardener.

Artificial fertilizer is not necessary, with the possible exception of lime and trace elements, if all the above conditions are observed – first and foremost, if the plants are well mulched. But an occasional application of liquid manure when the buds are developing in autumn will do no harm.

Hellebores in Winter

The behaviour of young hybrid seedlings in the hardest winter conditions has already been described. Adult plants are not quite as tough, but they can be helped by some adaptations. In a similar manner to the nocturnal movements of French beans, *Helleborus foetidus* bends its leaves, and also each leaflet at its base, when it is frozen. This does not seem to be due to dry soil, i.e. it is obviously not caused by lack of water, since when temperatures rise the leaves and leaflets lift up again. It is only when there are harder frosts that the stem and inflorescence as a whole shrivel and go flaccid, something that happens with the flower stems of all other hellebores.

In the winter of 1984/85, *Helleborus × nigercors* was the hero among the hellebores: there was no snow, but intermittent frost to −16°C (3°F) and its leaves, which were a glossy green at the start, became a dull greyish-green with distinct white veins, but its functions did not appear to be affected. In milder spells the inflorescence grew on slowly. The leaves were just a little flabby, but not sharply bent like those of *H. foetidus*. However, this plant is growing in a spot shaded by the house in winter and sheltered from cutting northerly and easterly winds. In the following winters *H. × nigercors* behaved in the same way, in spite of temperatures that occasionally fell as low as −25°C (−13°F). Under such circumstances

this hybrid is hardier than either of its parents, *H. niger* and *H. argutifolius*.

Helleborus × sternii is similarly hardy, but I can only give proof of this in the case of a special plant of the F₂ generation, which has inherited the very early flowering of *H. lividus*. This plant is named 'Wintersilber' as it lacks the pink undersides to the leaves and tepals of the F₁ hybrid, having silvery-green leaves and yellow-green flowers. It too is hardier than its parents but is also growing in winter shade.

For almost all the month of February 1986, 10 cm (4 in) of snow covered the garden and very often the temperatures were between −10°C (14°F) and −20°C (−4°F). During this period the leaves of *Helleborus niger* plants that stood in the sun were destroyed by frost. When at last the snow thawed they were a black-green slime. Leaves of *H. niger* plants that had the protection of a mulch of compost beneath the snow stayed green and healthy. Even tender light green shoots that were covered by mulch were not damaged in any way, whether in shade or in sun. On the other hand, a covering of conifer branches did not help plants that were standing in the sun.

Helleborus niger, in particular, needs protection from a mulch or unbroken day-long shade in cold winters, but this species also shows characters that must be regarded as adaptations to low temperatures. At −2°C (28°F) to −3°C (26°F) *H. niger* plants are affected, the flower stems first of all, but the leaves too droop slightly or even lie flat on the ground as if killed by the frost. At about 0°C (32°F) they slowly stand up again. How do they manage this? Do the leaves and flower stems temporarily lose water? Is the water drawn from the upper part of the plant by osmosis? These events occur frequently in most winters, but when they happen too often they finally damage the plant: first the flower stems and, much later, the leaves are destroyed. It is probable that the damage is done by lack of water, as most of the available water is frozen. On sandy heath soils this happens quite often.

Other species, even *Helleborus lividus* in a small way, reveal the same abilities before they succumb to frost. The 'winter-bare' Europeans are an exception; they protect themselves very effectively by voluntarily shedding their upper parts.

Helleborus lividus, when growing in the open in northern Germany, has all its parts above ground (but only those) destroyed by frost, a regular catastrophe happening almost every winter. The only new stem the plant can develop afterwards is never taller than a two-year-old seedling and never flowers, as it needs all the strength it can gather in its short life-span just to stay alive. How long this species can continue to exist in this way is unknown, but mine has survived at least eight years with temperatures occasionally down to −25°C (−13°F).

If *Helleborus argutifolius* is growing in a sunny place with no protection it will be badly frozen in hard winters. The stem cracks below the leaves and is unable to develop the flowers properly. After the flowering season it grows normal stems, which do not remain stunted like those of *H. lividus* because *H. argutifolius* does not suffer in this way regularly every year. So this species is valuable as a foliage plant or can even be regarded as a dwarf shrub, all year, in spite of occasional frost damage.

Helleborus foetidus too suffers in cold winters, particularly in sunny spots. The stems are frozen at the base of the inflorescence and snap off at this point. With this hellebore the development of the flowers is also affected, but there seem to be differences between one plant and another. *H. foetidus* takes advantage of every mild spell to develop its flowers.

The Lenten Roses or *Helleborus orientalis* hybrids are very hardy. All are winter-green and generally have large, very hard leaves. Winter brings the end of the season for these leaves and they wither gradually and slowly, which is normal. The species grow in the hills and mountains of regions with winter rain where the temperature sometimes drops to freezing point. Light frosts kill their flower stems and those of their hybrids much earlier than the leaves, which are still standing upright and strong, so strong that they often lose their leaflets to wind rather than to frost. They stand above the flowers when these are laid low by frost so that when the snow comes, the flowers are covered by it long before the leaves, which although they will soon reach the end of their lives are still important as protection for the flowers. Sometimes they fall outwards and lie around the flower stems on the ground. It may be a good idea to tie them up in a bunch so that they continue their protective function.

What does damage the Lenten Roses and, of course, the true *Helleborus orientalis* species, are the severe late frosts that come just when the plants are most actively developing their flower stems. The combination of frost at night and spring warmth during the day does hardly any damage to the large old leaves, but is very damaging to the young tissue of the growing flower stems. It is really necessary to provide winter cover for them at such times. So take precautions until all possibility of late frosts is over!

Anyone who has ever grown a batch of seedlings from a Lenten Rose knows that these siblings may show different degrees of hardiness. The package of genes contributed by each parent, male and female, can be very complex, depending on the number of different ancestors. Observe the seedlings very carefully, keeping the parents' characters in mind, and eliminate the weak ones. A flower may be the most beautiful one possible, but it will bring nothing but trouble if it is not at least of average hardiness so that it will remain unharmed in milder winters.

Unless the plants are specifically required for growing under glass, one should not try to breed very early-flowering cultivars as their flower stems will fall victim to the winter much more readily than those that flower later. Frost does great damage to these flowers and also reduces their numbers. In addition, it seems that fungal disease often follows frost damage. It is also not really worthwhile collecting those hybrids that produce precocious flowers from July and August onwards, as in most cases they do not have time to open all their flowers before winter kills them. They are papery and dry when the normal flowers are in full bloom. Nor are they suitable for cutting as they have different, less attractive colours and forms than spring flowers on the same plant. It is not worth bothering to select them unless the aim is to breed a race of 'Indian Summer' hellebores.

Apart from the damaged flower stems, it must be said that the plants recover quite well from the onslaughts of winter and later in the year show no trace of their ordeal. They are particularly happy under a thick blanket of snow. From this one can deduce what a hellebore needs for plentiful and lovely spring bloom. If such snow cover is not available, then a substitute for it must be provided in cold regions.

It is not easy to do this for the stemmed hellebores as they are too tall, but there is a proven method at least for *Helleborus argutifolius*, one also used for standard roses. The stems of this hellebore lie down around the plant in spring to make way for the new shoots. We make them do this by weighing them down with large branches of conifers before frost and snow arrive. If harder frosts are likely to threaten the plant later on, it gets a warm but light covering of a suitable mulch, or more conifer branches. But be careful when you try to straighten the stems! It is better to wait for a few days, as they easily break at the base. This method has not been tried on heavy, sticky, cold soil but it works well in warm sandy gardens.

All the other hellebores, including the 'winter-bare' ones, get a thick covering of mulch, if possible. Spent mushroom compost from a commercial mushroom grower is particularly valuable, but larch needles or light compost are also very good. Peat can be used but should be avoided if possible because of the need to halt the exhaustion of peat bogs. The cover can be fairly thick as there is no reason to fear that the plants will be damaged as long as it is light and airy. But after the cold winter, when spring comes, it is advisable to draw the mulch away, as otherwise the warmth will speed up the growth of the flower stems. It will then be difficult to cover them if late frosts return, as may well happen. The old leaves do not need this sort of covering; only the centre of the plant, where new buds will be growing, is covered with the deep layer of mulch. Unfortunately one never knows in advance whether to prepare for a mild or a hard winter! If the number of plants is not too great, the mulch can be laid around them to start with and later, when it becomes necessary, it can be moved to cover the buds. Further experience in this matter will, it is hoped, lead to improved methods.

A good depth of mulch has other advantages. As well as taking the place of snow, it fertilizes the soil and helps to retain moisture in spring. Many earthworms live in it and draw the coarser material down into the soil, eventually producing a more open texture. The mulch also discourages early weeds, until they can be shaded out by the new leaves of the hellebores themselves. Finally, by midsummer, the mulch will have broken down into a layer of humus only 1 mm ($\frac{1}{24}$ in) thick.

It is fascinating to watch hellebore plants during the winter and see how they cope with or fight against the hardships of the season, and eventually triumph even if only in a small way. And it is satisfying to help them and see them respond.

To cheer up anyone who thinks that all this is far too much hard work, it can be said that hellebores will live and even flower without all this attention. There will be fewer flowers and their colour will not be unblemished, but one can enjoy whatever has survived the winter's trials. Or move to a garden in a warmer region!

Pests and Diseases

Animal and insect pests do not trouble the hellebore grower very much. The larvae of a leaf-mining moth may be seen, mostly on *Helleborus niger*, but only relatively seldom. Greenfly (aphides) can sometimes be found on the petioles of young seedlings, or on adult plants if they are crowded too close together. All these have to be dealt with by the usual methods but, above all, by good plant care as hellebores are then practically free from pests.

If, now and then, after a long hard winter, a little mouse nibbles the flower buds, it probably does so because it gets a medicine from them – well, we can bear that. But it is quite a different matter when the tiny snails (both those with pointed and those with flat shells) about 5 mm ($\frac{1}{4}$ in) in diameter, which live in their billions on the heathland, chew the surface of the leaves leaving only a thin white membrane. They always prefer the hellebores with thinner leaves. This does not seem to harm the plants in any way but it looks very unsightly. Unfortunately, none of the usual methods of control work with these snails. The gardener's best helpers are probably the birds.

Stunted growth and weak sprouting of new leaves, mainly seen on *Helleborus niger*, are dangerous. In private gardens such plants should not be allowed to remain but are better burnt because, unless these symptoms can be corrected by improved cultivation, they are probably caused by wandering root nematodes (eelworm) that will quickly attack other plants as well. If these signs appear in a nursery, the advice of the Plant Health Inspector should be sought.

Much more devastating than all the damage that animals or insects can do are the attacks by primitive fungi. These result not only in ugly black and brown, large and small spots but also in the breakdown of large areas of tissue. As well as looking unpleasant, the plant may be so badly harmed that in certain circumstances it may be completely destroyed. When the earliest signs of infestation show up as the first little spots, it is best to start an immediate programme to eliminate it if this has not already been done as a preventive measure. The species and hybrids most susceptible are *Helleborus niger* and its relatives, *H. guttatus* and its hybrids, and *H. multifidus*.

All parts of the plant must be included in the treatment, as all of them can be infected. Every bit of infected tissue must be rigorously removed and burnt. A generous dressing of lime and trace elements is then worked into the soil around the plant without damaging the roots. This should be well watered in. When the plant is dry again, all parts are sprayed with a fungicide, not forgetting the undersides of the leaves. After that the plants should be watched very carefully until every sign of the fungus has gone in case repeat sprayings are necessary. If plants are so heavily infected that it seems impossible to cure them, they should be dug up and burnt at once.

In most cases the cause of this black spot disease is *Coniothyrium*. This fungus produces black-brown spots that spread from the margins of the leaves towards the centre. *Coniothyrium* also affects petioles and pedicels. In summer this disease is spread from plant to plant by spores; in winter the spores hide on affected plants. The infection is encouraged by the wrong planting site, wrong soil pH and fertilizer too high in nitrogen.

When young petioles suddenly collapse in spring, the cause is probably a bud, rhizome and stem-base rot caused by *Rhizoctonia solani*. This can be dealt with by the usual fungicidal controls.

False Honeydew frequently occurs, especially in nurseries that specialize in growing *Helleborus niger* for cut flowers. This produces crippled spotty leaves with a grey film on the underside. Another symptom is small, grey-brown premature flowers. This fungus, *Peronospora pulveracea*, also overwinters on sickly leaves. Unfortunately it cannot be eliminated by any of the usual fungicides, because it lives deep in the rhizome, so these plants must be burnt.

Of course some of the phenomena described may simply be an indication of poor health caused by wrong treatment. In this case prompt transplantation to another spot may be helpful. But it is advisable anyway, especially when there is more than one plant in the garden, that they should be regularly sprayed with fungicide in spring when they start into growth, and again in autumn.

There may also, possibly, be virus diseases. In some years *Helleborus niger* and also, but rarely, some hybrids, have strange-looking deeply serrated leaves with an irregularly coloured whitish margin. As this does not appear each year on one and the same plant, it cannot be a mutation. So far there is no treatment for virus diseases. The best procedure is to dig up the whole plant, burn it, and not to plant a hellebore in that spot again. If the plant should happen to be important for hybridizing, then it must be isolated. Viruses are probably not transmitted by seed, but only by contact.

With the exception of *Coniothyrium* on *Helleborus niger*, especially 'Praecox', the diseases and pests described above do not occur too often. Well-cared-for, healthy plants are always the most resistant to all these troubles. If, at some time, completely neglected plants must be treated, information should also be sought on nematodes and pests that may attack the roots of hellebores.

Use in the Garden

Looking at all the good features of hellebores, one asks in astonishment why these perennials, so excellent as garden plants, are in practice so seldom seen? In a large garden there may perhaps be a shady area where they can be allowed to naturalize, but this does not exhaust their potential uses. They should be given suitable sites that are easily accessible, especially in winter and spring, to the public. Keen gardeners are willing to travel far and wide to see, for instance, the marvellous blue flowers of *Meconopsis betonicifolia* in Scottish gardens. I can imagine that the richness of the blood-red or the 'exotic' black *Helleborus* flowers, if displayed in suitable settings in famous large gardens, could equally well entice keen gardeners from afar. Moreover, as well as black and red, other colours and more surprises could be made better known.

It would, of course, be necessary for large nurseries selling perennials to make a greater effort than they already do to produce these beautiful and hardy plants in large numbers. These public gardens could become very special events in late winter and early spring, lifting the spirits of people wearied by winter. These suggestions might also, I hope, stimulate many garden owners and encourage more enthusiasts to grow these plants.

Sadly, the current position is hardly ideal. In some reputable gardens the so-called Christmas Rose can be found and at best one, maybe two or three, Lenten Roses, usually self-sown seedlings without names. Few people today can find space in their gardens for hellebores to naturalize as they do in large gardens, as a single plant becomes large and spreading in the course of its long life. But perhaps we can use them in other ways?

Certainly every garden, particularly when it is well established, has more than one shady place. It would be delightful if the genus in its different guises could impress itself more deeply on the minds of keen gardeners and take the place among other shade-loving perennials it deserves. Surely a few hellebores would add cheerful spots of colour to each shady border in spring – provided one likes their colours.

Perhaps one of the reasons why hellebores are only sparingly used in our gardens lies in their flower colours. The few new cultivars with intense uniform hues of glowing red, shining purple, soft pink and primrose yellow are still not widely known. The gentle, sometimes too restrained hues of the older kinds do not associate well with strong colours, but the pretty new cultivars, too, always remain modest and unassuming. They must not be mixed with modern tulips and the new daffodils. The large gaudy polyanthus are, in most cases, not suitable companions for hellebores, either. But as shade is not generally liked by these brightly-coloured flowers, hellebores can take over in the shady parts of the garden in association with suitable plants at a time when they are at their best. They have the number and size of flowers, and the imposing stature, to do this.

Four questions face us when we think of how and where to integrate hellebores into our gardens:

1. Which hellebore is best for which purpose?
2. Which plants can be combined with hellebores that will flower at the same time?
3. Which plants will present an agreeable picture throughout the year through their leaf shapes and colours?
4. For which later-flowering plants will hellebores make a good foil?

We shall have to keep these questions in mind when considering the following suggestions.

There is a small, mixed group of hellebores that find themselves grouped together simply because of their early flowering time. It would not be at all a bad idea to grow all these 'Christmas Roses' (or, better, precocious forms) together in a very sheltered spot close to the house, so as to be able to visit them in the worst weather without getting one's feet cold or wet, or, if necessary, to care for them. A small inner courtyard would be ideal. Into it one could bring *Helleborus niger* 'Praecox', 'Atrorubens' ('Early Purple'), 'Galathé', a few early-flowering forms of *H. orientalis* and early Lenten Roses, *H. dumetorum*, *H. multifidus* in the form of

Schiffner's *H. siculus*, and a few early *H. niger* subsp. *macranthus*. Containers holding *H. lividus* could stand there until the first frost. Snowdrops and winter aconites (*Eranthis hiemalis*) would cover the ground beneath the hellebores.

If there is a wall to be covered, *Jasminum nudiflorum* fits in wonderfully, in sun or shade. A shady wall could be embellished with varieties of ivy such as 'Goldheart', 'Sagittifolia' on a white wall, 'Buttercup' or the lovely 'Angularis Aurea' on a wall of brownish-red brick. Slow-growing ground-covering ivies like 'Caecilia' could also grow at the front of a shady bed while *Erica* 'Winterbeauty' or similar early-flowering cultivars could occupy the same position on the sunny side. A few stemmed hellebores and a *Daphne* would find adequate quarters in the background. This could be a winter garden in the literal meaning of the words.

In other seasons the little courtyard could be used, in a similar way, as a sanctuary for tender but lime-loving treasures like some of the lilies, or for container plants like *Abutilon*, *Hebe speciosa* or a collection of fuchsias. Perennials such as *Dictamnus albus* and some euphorbias that are not really hardy could also be tried here. The hellebores would provide a green foil for all these plants throughout the year.

This foil could, of course, be made even richer by interplanting with perennials or small shrubs, which would brighten the scene in the hellebore season by their colourful leaves, for example Bergenias such as the small-leaved *B. purpurascens* or beautiful cultivars; *Tellima grandiflora* with bronze-veined leaves; young *Barbarea vulgaris* 'Variegata' with green and white leaves, looking lovely with snowdrops in its first year. Brave gardeners with well-protected courtyards, or those in suitable climates, could perhaps risk planting an *Elaeagnus* such as *E. macrophylla* or *E. pungens* 'Maculata'. Or *Euonymus japonicus* 'Ovatus Albus' ('Argentea-Variegatus') would fit in very well.

Hepaticas, daphnes, heathers, *Lathyrus vernus*, early violas and a great variety of small bulbs all flower at the same time as other *Helleborus* species, so there is no lack of partners and possibilities for companion plantings.

Of course it is also possible to mass hellebores of different flower colours, but that is not recommended for the small garden as the mass of green leaves, too large in relation to the size of the garden, will be monotonous and boring later in the season. It is always better to allow each hellebore plant to be seen as an individual plant surrounded by smaller flowers.

The easiest way for the beginner to start is by planting the hybrids, the Lenten Roses. It is important to find those that are best for the garden among all the different colour variations. There are flowers that are green, white, cream, primrose, porcelain pink, deep pink, lilac-pink, red, dark red, brown-red, black-red, metallic blue, pink with brownish-red dots, white with spots, greenish-yellow with spots, and still more. The spots can be small or large, scattered like dust over the whole flower or arranged in eyes, ray-coronas or patches. The flowers are small or large, shallow or deep bowls, which are drooping, nodding or face us. The inflorescences are few- or many-flowered, the plants are small or large, imposing or dainty. In short, there are Lenten Roses for almost every place in the garden. But a temptation that should be resisted as strongly as possible is to combine them with common, colourful garden perennials. As exotic as, in fact, the hellebores may appear in some cases, they do not go well together with these plants, but are always plants for the more natural part of the garden.

In lighter borders with dappled shade, the dark green and typically-shaped Lenten Rose leaves can be complemented by perennials with coloured leaves, as for example *Cimicifuga simplex* 'Brunette', variegated hostas of medium size, *Astrantia major* 'Sunningdale Variegated', and many more. Hostas, in particular, come in wonderful forms nowadays, though unfortunately not all are readily available from nurseries. Those cultivars with blue and light yellow leaves must be used especially carefully. Most need full shade to protect their beautifully coloured leaves. Grasses, both green and coloured ones, enliven the hellebore plantings.

Ferns are a must, for with their filigree foliage in varying shades of green, romance enters the garden. A rock or a moss-covered tree stump adds the finishing touch. Anyone who has discovered how much atmosphere is introduced into a garden by these means will regret having too few shady places.

Martagon lilies, American Bellingham hybrid lilies and their relations, *Anemone* × *hybrida* (Japanese Anemones), *Kirengeshoma palmata*, all kinds of *Pulmonaria*, *Lamium* in attractive varieties, *Omphalodes* and many more perennials with pretty flowers can also be combined with hellebores, which can be underplanted with snowdrops and winter aconites.

The top candidate for a winter garden is *Helleborus foetidus*. As a foliage plant, an isolated specimen is unbeatable with its blackish-green, finely cut, palm-like leaves and the bulky yellowish-green clubs of the buds containing the inflorescences. When it stands in the snow on a sunny day in late winter or spring, with two or three early crocuses and the bees on their first spring flights bumbling about as if drunk on its pollen-tassels, it can make even an indifferent and grumpy garden visitor stop and ask, curiously, what it is. It is equally good either as an isolated plant or as a background plant and it also fits very well into a border of larger perennials. The seedlings that crop up all around the edges of the

bed adapt themselves to their surroundings, but are easily removed if they are not wanted. It hardly needs to be said that after a few years there are many more of them in the garden than were originally intended! After a while, one comes to understand just how beautiful and, at the same time, useful they are.

The Corsican Hellebore, *Helleborus argutifolius*, is a little less versatile. It could almost be regarded as a dwarf shrub and this is just how it should be used. When planted in a sunny spot, it develops a more compact shape as the leaves on each stem form a convex dome. Gardeners, however, frequently have to do without the flowers because they are killed by frost if they grow where they get sun in winter. In the shade, its handsome architectural shape is more or less lost. In most years the stems lie down on the ground in a wide circle or semicircle so that the new stems in the centre receive enough light. It is possible to straighten them and tie them up, which saves valuable space as the Corsican Hellebore is a fairly imposing plant. As a foliage plant it always looks good and is particularly well placed in the area between an informal hedge and the border.

The lower-growing *Helleborus* × *sternii*, which has more attractively-coloured flowers, can be used in a similar way, but in addition can be planted as an isolated plant or in the border, as with *H. foetidus*. If it is allowed to seed around, some charming seedlings can often be found which sometimes, as for instance in 'Wintersilber', combine a very early flowering period with the greater vigour of *H. argutifolius*. So they can take the place of *H. lividus* and *H. foetidus* if an early-flowering plant is needed to associate with the precocious forms.

Narrow borders on the north side of a house can be designed using the stemmed hellebores instead of conifer hedges, which are planted far too often. Stemmed hellebores are planted at the back of the bed, with low-growing silvery biennials such as *Senecio cineraria* at the front, or perennials with silvery leaves such as varieties of *Lamium*. This does not, of course, mean that it is impossible to combine hellebores and conifers. At the edge of a group of dwarf conifers, *Helleborus niger* looks particularly good and creates a pleasing picture in association with heathers, hepaticas and daphnes.

No-one should ever miss a chance of growing *Helleborus niger* 'Praecox', for although it is a difficult and capricious companion, it does flower reliably from the end of September. The best way to plant it is in company with *Saxifraga cortusifolia* var. *fortunei* in places that attract attention when, apart from these two, there are only a few roses, such as 'The Fairy', still carrying some flowers. It may be worthwhile adding a few of the blue-leaved hostas, which in some years clothe themselves in glowing autumn colours, or planting some colchicums if there is sufficient light. In this way

the garden can produce a last little firework display.

In mild winters *Helleborus niger* subsp. *macranthus* starts to flower in January, providing one has selected early-flowering forms. The flowers are still hidden by the leaves, though some specimens show off their flowers by spreading their large leaves out in all directions. In mild winters their snowy blooms are especially immaculate and sparkle in the sun. If the weather is less kind, the flowers can delay their appearance until March. This hellebore, in contrast to *H. niger* 'Praecox', is not at all fussy and repays good care by showing its full glory. If, therefore, the intention is to have a spring festival of flower with *H. niger*, this subspecies is the best partner for bulbs and heathers, but it can also be associated with *H.* × *nigercors*, *H.* × *sternii* or *H. foetidus*, especially in the exceptional form 'Wester Flisk', which was found in Scotland and which comes true from seed.

Helleborus × *nigercors* is an impressive plant when mature and at the height of its eye-catching, undeniably decorative effect, which lasts for such a long time that even late, delicately flowered primulas such as 'Lady Greer' or 'Kinlough Beauty' can sometimes be planted beside it. When it is combined with *H. foetidus*, *H. argutifolius* and *H.* × *sternii*, splendid winter and spring groupings are the result, their different greens shining out across the garden. Nor should it be forgotten that they will continue to look attractive for the rest of the year. With blue-flowered bulbous iris, they give pleasure to those who like cool colours. Those who want something brighter can add *Fritillaria imperialis* and dwarf *Narcissus*.

Helleborus lividus has to lead a solitary life since it is not fully hardy, at least not in colder areas. To be precise, the winter does not kill the underground part of the plant, but it is unlikely that there will ever be a winter that is so mild that the surface stem and the flower buds will survive. Even if a plant, which has been weakened by suffering repeated doses of this harsh treatment, should manage to produce a small flower bud, it will never come into flower in the open.

However, a well-cared-for *Helleborus lividus* will develop wonderfully as a container plant. During the warmer weather, i.e. until the first frost arrives, stand it in the garden or on the terrace. Indoors its effect can be enhanced by a few branches of Scots Pine or, as an alternative, a plant of *H.* 'Atrorubens' brought in from outside.

The European hellebore species not amongst those already mentioned have not been much tried in gardens because it is usually difficult to obtain them. Germination of seed is sparse and growing them on reveals that they grow slowly. They still have to prove their worth in the garden, though it would be truer to say that we do not yet know what they like. It is even rumoured that they suffer

from root rot, a condition otherwise unknown amongst hellebores.

They can be used in the same ways as their relatives, but it will probably be found that some or all of them need more warmth or even some sun, at least in summer. Trials to discover this should perhaps not be made with *Helleborus purpurascens* which is a woodland plant, but *H. cyclophyllus*, *H. odorus* or *H. multifidus* subsp. *bocconei* could possibly be suitable. They could be planted in the light shade of deciduous shrubs, where *H. torquatus* could also be tried. Hermann Fuchs even recommends that they be used to provide shade for *Lilium jankae* and other lilies from the Balkans. The *H. multifidus* with particularly beautiful leaves, subsp. *hercegovinus*, could certainly be used for this purpose, and also *H. viridis*. As lilies grow in sunny, exposed places, *H. multifidus* subsp. *bocconei* should probably not be used, and especially not the form from Sicily, as they could be somewhat tender. But this is a field wide open for experiments by the adventurous gardener.

Helleborus multifidus, whose leaves are many-lobed and also very variable in their overall form, is well suited for display in the garden as a particularly interesting foliage plant, as has been said. One form collected by the Fuchs family in Yugoslavia has a leaf that is not only multi-lobed (38 leaflets on a still young plant) but is also almost symmetrical in form, like an acanthus leaf. Not all of them have such distinguished form, but all bring a change in design and should be used for the sake of their shape, as the greenish-yellow flowers are rather inconspicuous. Some that do not become too big are suitable for planting with relatives that flower at the same time and have reddish leaves or red flowers, like 'Torquatus', or to give the essential background to a large group of *Hepatica*.

In its best forms *Helleborus multifidus* is an outstanding foliage plant that, especially in spring when the young leaves are reminiscent of little palm trees, attracts attention from passersby. But its summer foliage is also most effective and always interesting, never out of place.

Apart from *Helleborus multifidus* in its Sicilian form, *H. cyclophyllus* reaches furthest to the south. This plant is rumoured to start flowering very late. Maybe this has something to do with its need for warmth. It is also said to need more lime than its relatives. When planting it in an appropriate spot, one should think of siting it so as to make effective use of the silvery hairs on the undersides of the leaves, which are present or can be seen only as long as the leaves are folded together.

The large, yellow-green, bowl-shaped flowers of *Helleborus cyclophyllus* and *H. odorus* bring a cheerful note into the spring garden; they are enhanced by *Primula* 'Wanda Improved', bright blue *Scilla* species or anything with early blue flowers. As *H. odorus* also comes

from the warm hills and mountains of the Balkans and therefore likes warm sunshine, there are possible companions other than scillas and other small bulbs: for instance, double primroses in delicate blue, white and yellow can be tried. All these early perennials are small so that the hellebores by their stately size alone bring a welcome change and variation in height to the spring picture.

With *Helleborus dumetorum* it must be borne in mind that as the leaves emerge very early, perennials planted beneath it will not get much sun. Only *Eranthis hiemalis* and similar 'early birds' can grow with it. This hellebore, with its many small green flowers, is better suited than all the other species to being surrounded by other perennial wild flowers, or forming a background for small ones. The red-flowered *H. atrorubens* probably requires a little more warmth and drier conditions than *H. dumetorum*, although it has almost the same area of distribution, just not reaching quite so far north. Unlike the green species its leaves develop late, during or after the flowering season, so it can be underplanted.

Here I should like to say a little more about the red-flowered form of *Helleborus torquatus*, i.e. the selected form 'Torquatus' described earlier. Experiences from 1984 to 1987 have shown that this plant is very well suited for the cold winters of northern Germany (to date it has not been sufficiently tested in mild ones).

The foliage dies in November-December but the flower stems are slowly pushing up as early as February. During this period it likes to have overhead shade from leaves, for instance from a winter-green fern. The dainty flowers open in the first 10 days of April and the plant is beautiful in a very graceful way. All its parts are red. The radical leaves come up later, so it could be underplanted with cowslips, which are at their best at the same time and would complement it very well.

Helleborus purpurascens is rather small at the beginning of the flowering season. It starts in March when the flower stem is only 2–3 cm ($\frac{3}{4}$–$1\frac{1}{8}$ in) high, but of course it grows taller. Each stem usually only bears three flowers. This hellebore could be used on the shady side of a rock garden or in the foreground of a shady border, but the leaves eventually become rather large.

I have not had much success with *Helleborus* 'Intermedius', which increases extraordinarily slowly. It seems to stay rather small and starts to flower much later than other hellebores, namely in the fourth year after planting.

I cannot say anything about the beauty of the flowers, the garden value of the plant or suggest suitable planting places. It remains to be seen how well this hellebore adapts itself and if it proves successful as, in its sixth year, it again failed to flower.

Use in Flower Arranging and Floristry

Compared with their degree of popularity, the Christmas Roses, *Helleborus niger* 'Praecox', are too seldom seen in ordinary nurseries to explain the source of the flood of white flowers around Christmas. And a few days later they have as suddenly gone again, as if someone had called them away.

There are special nurseries where *Helleborus niger* is grown in large glasshouses, producing much bigger and more beautiful flowers than it can ever attain in the average garden. They are forced into flower at just the right time, so that they are on sale at the beginning of Advent and a continual supply is available until Christmas. In business this is called timing. In this case it is done with living, delicate flowers, not with inanimate products, which obviously creates some difficulties.

First, it is necessary to have plants that can be brought into flower at exactly the right moment. As clones of *Helleborus niger* can vary widely in their flowering times, one clone can be more suitable than another. If the plants are grown from seed, they will have to be selected, a process taking about four years. It also takes a long time to produce an adequate stock of plants from a few selected forms, as two to four years must be allowed for a piece of such a plant to flower again. Unfortunately it is not generally possible to buy, say, 500 plants of a good form but they have

to be obtained by sowing, selecting and lengthy propagation. The famous selections of Bold and Haller were created in this way. Today, sadly, most nurseries do not take this time and trouble, but only sow seed, grow the plants that happen to fit their timing and sell the rest as pot plants, all at the expense of quality.

How do high-quality Christmas Roses have to be grown? The planting compost has already been discussed. The temperature must not be too high, the air must be sufficiently moist but not too much so, and the drainage must be excellent. Good feeding is important, but too much nitrogen should be avoided as this encourages infection by fungal diseases as does too much sun. Too much mineral fertilizer is also harmful. In limited light the plants grow longer flower stems and larger, whiter blooms.

When forcing begins, the plants must be completely covered with black cloths for a fortnight and the temperature is increased very slowly. For example, from 10–20 November it is raised from 4°C (39°F) to 8°C (46°F) until, at the beginning of December, it is increased to 6–10°C (43–50°F). In the final days the plants get 12–16°C (54–60°F), depending on what is necessary. Moisture from condensation must be strictly avoided, so growers do not use black plastic sheeting for covering.

As soon as the outer ring of stamens sheds pollen, harvesting of the flowers begins. They must be cut, not broken off, and can be stored at

1–2°C (34–36°F). The literature on the subject states that by using this method they will keep from November to December. They must be watered again before being delivered.

Depending on the quality of the cultivar and manner of forcing – growing in the open, under mobile glasshouses and in frames are all also practised – from 10 to 70 flower stems may be gathered from one plant. When harvesting is over, the plants can, if necessary, be divided and replanted.

As well as *Helleborus niger*, the red-flowered *H.* 'Atrorubens' is suitable for cultivation as a pot plant. Small or young plants are potted into 11–13 cm ($4\frac{3}{4}$–5 in) pots for this purpose. From the beginning of November they are kept at 8–12°C (46–54°F). They are not forced, as they are used for decoration in cool rooms. The early-flowering Lenten Roses can also be tried as pot plants. Schiffner states that *H. orientalis* subsp. *guttatus* is also very suitable, but only with a normal amount of light.

Other hellebores, in addition to Christmas Roses and 'Atrorubens', are useful to flower arrangers. The stemmed species provide leaves, particularly the exquisite black-green ones of *Helleborus foetidus*. Single, fresh leaves are cut, but complete stems can also be used. These must be split at the base, the ends held in boiling water for two minutes, and then be kept floating or plunged in water until they are used. *Helleborus foetidus, H. lividus* and *H. argutifolius* can be stored for a long time in this manner if they are cut in winter.

The leaves can also be preserved with glycerine for much longer, so as to have them always at hand for arrangements. To do this, prepare a mixture of $\frac{1}{3}$ glycerine and $\frac{2}{3}$ hot water and immerse the leaves totally in a flat container. After one to two weeks they will change colour, indicating that they are ready. If they are slimy, they must be carefully washed in lukewarm water, then dried equally carefully and stored in the dark. Protect them against moisture, heat, moulds and rot; the best way to do this is to keep them in boxes between sheets of absorbent paper, as otherwise they will easily go musty.

Helleborus buds are not suitable for cutting as they die immediately. The flowers must be mature and have to be cut as early in the morning as possible. The Lenten Roses are not generally suitable for cutting, but experience has shown that trials should be made, as an unimportant seedling can sometimes prove suitable as a cut flower. It also depends on the temperature of the day, the time of cutting, and particularly on the following treatment.

I have found that flowers from *H. multifidus* seedlings are very suitable for cutting. The cut flowers should never at any time be kept out of water, unless they are kept very cool. Therefore it is best to take a container of lukewarm water into the garden when a bunch of flowers is to be cut. The flower stems are slit along one side for their full length, from the flower to the base, with a sharp knife. The skin of the stem is covered with wax, but they can take up enough water through the slit. After that, the bases of the stems are placed in boiling water for two minutes, the flower heads protected by being wrapped in paper or a cloth. They are then stood in deep lukewarm water until they are used.

Mature flowers of the Corsican Hellebore are also very useful. Even when they have gone limp, they can be revived by plunging them in lukewarm water until they return to normal.

Among other plant material that combines well with hellebores, bergenia leaves and those of variegated ivies are excellent. Many ivies sold as pot plants prove to be hardy when tried in the garden. Winter-flowering heathers are also very good, of course, as are *Jasminum nudiflorum*, branches of *Rhododendron* and *Euonymus*, and winter-green ferns such as *Blechnum spicant* and staghorn fern. The leaves and seedpods of *Iris foetidissima* are beautiful and decorative for a very long time.

Bouquets and arrangements with hellebores are not suitable for centrally-heated rooms. They are best kept in cool places. At the very least they should be put in an unheated room overnight. It goes without saying that they must always have adequate water.

If all these conditions are met, a hellebore arrangement will last literally for several months. For example, a bowl with *Helleborus niger*, *H. lividus*, *H. × sternii* and complementary plant material was made up on 28 January. On 26 February some branches of *Jasminum nudiflorum* were replaced by *Cornus mas* and on 5 April the whole arrangement was dismantled. During this time the hellebore flowers only changed as they would have done had they remained on the living plants; they looked good all the time. Of course, throughout this period, the bowl stood in a cool but sunny, unheated, enclosed porch and was kept full of water.

Helleborus in Medicine

Hellebores are very obviously avoided by grazing animals as they are poisonous. However, they have been cultivated since the Middle Ages for medicinal purposes. This explains why they have spread so far beyond their original homelands. They first became naturalized from monastery gardens and, later, from farm gardens. Thus it is that we cannot say for certain whether a plant occurs naturally or is a naturalized escape from cultivation. So, for example, in Germany *Helleborus foetidus* grows around Jena and in the Harz; *Helleborus niger* can be found in Württemberg, Bavaria, Thüringen, near the Rhine, in the Tyrol and in Bohemia; and *H. viridis* is recorded from some places in the north lowlands. Such occurrences must all be investigated very thoroughly before they can be proclaimed as natural habitats.

These herbs went from the hands of the knowledgeable monks to those of farmers who used them as medicine for their sick animals, and finally they were offered on fairgrounds by charlatans as 'wonder cures', said to be 'useful to purge or purify the body of all the evil and unwholesome superfluities'.

Helleborus was also used in classical Greece, and probably even earlier, as a medicinal plant, but it is doubtful whether any distinction was made between the different species, as was probably also the case in the Middle Ages. We now know that they do not always contain the same chemical substances or, if they are the same, they are not in the same concentrations. These herbs were very often associated with healing properties they do not possess. For example, *Helleborus niger* was used in herbal mixtures, but does not have any medicinal properties whatsoever.

In ancient times, and even up to the present day, *Helleborus* has been used as a treatment for lunacy, paralytic symptoms and epilepsy, and a strong purgative. So, for example, Drusus was cured of epilepsy in Anticyra by *Helleborus*, probably *H. orientalis* in this case, and Hercules is said to have been healed of an attack of lunacy. Between 160 and 180 A.D. Pausanias wrote *Periegsis tes Hellados*, a book about his travels, in which is a report on the use of *Helleborus* in Greece. Even today, using this as a guide is probably more useful and less dangerous than some methods currently practised.

In Book 10, Chapter 37, Pausanias gives an example of early biological warfare: In order to fulfil a prophecy by the Oracle, Solon, the legislator and founder of democracy in Athens, wanted to dedicate the area around the town of Kirrha as a holy grove to Apollo. This upset the inhabitants and they began to fight. The Athenians first unsuccessfully besieged the town. Then Solon ordered the river Pleisthenes, from which the town got its drinking water, to be diverted. The besieged inhabitants had to make do with water from wells and rainfall. Meanwhile, Solon told his people to throw large amounts of hellebore roots, which grew abundantly in the area, into the river. When he thought that enough of the poison had leached into the water, he let the river revert to its old course. The town's citizens joyfully drank the fresh water they had been deprived of for so long. Unfortunately for them, they all, as a result, suffered such violent diarrhoea that they could no longer guard the town walls and they were conquered by the Athenians!

The drug *Rhizoma Hellebori*, i.e. the bark of the *Helleborus niger* rhizome, has long been used as a heart medicine. But the most recent findings reveal that it does not contain Hellebrin, which affects the heart, but only Helleborin, a strong purgative, and Protoanemonin, which irritates the mucous membranes. If, occasionally, symptoms of poisoning are reported, they are caused by the latter two substances, which are typical of the Ranunculaceae. Irritation of the mouth and throat, excessive amounts of saliva, vomiting, diarrhoea and dilation of the pupils of the eyes show that such poisoning

is present. If there is any suspicion that this is the case, the help of a doctor should be sought immediately. *Helleborus viridis* does, however, contain the strong heart drug Hellebrin, but also has a large amount of Helleborin. Hellebrin is used in homeopathic medicine, particularly to treat right-sided heart failure.

As, earlier, precise knowledge about the poisons and effects of the different hellebore species was lacking, the flowers of *Helleborus niger* were, quite senselessly, collected in their thousands, leading to the danger that this species would be wiped out. To prevent this it was made a protected species. Today hellebore species are no longer cultivated for medicinal purposes, human or animal, in private gardens. The dosage is far too difficult to determine and, therefore, its use is very dangerous, so the utilization of their healing properties is best left to professionals. It cannot be emphasized too strongly that no-one should ever try any medicinal experiments; they could very easily be fatal.

APPENDICES
BIBLIOGRAPHY

Ahlburg, M.: The seedling of *Helleborus vesicarius*, in *The Plantsman*, 9, 1: 18–20, 1987.

Anderson, E.B.: Hellebores, in *Journal of the Royal Horticultural Society*, 82, 279–293, 1957.

Anonymous: Über das Treiben von *Helleborus*, Gb + Gw 4, 76–81, 1983.

Ascherson, P. and Graebner, P.: *Synopsis der Mitteleuropäischen Flora*, Vol. 5/2, 587–609. Verlag Gebrüder Bornträger, Leipzig 1929.

Ballard, H.: Breeding a Yellow Hellebore, in *The Garden* 112: 45–46, 1987.

Czygan, F.C. and Kaiser, J.: *Jahreszeiten*. Hippokrates Verlag, Stuttgart, 1988.

Davis, P. and Cullen, J.: in *Flora of Turkey* 1: 96–97, 1965.

European Garden Flora, Vol. 3. Cambridge University Press, 1989.

Hegi, G.: *Illustrierte Flora von Mitteleuropa*. München 1965–1967.

Hess, D.: *Die Blüte*. Verlag Eugen Ulmer, Stuttgart, 1983.

Homöopathisches Repetitorium. Deutsche Homöopathische Union, Karlsruhe, 1984.

Koch, K.: Die Arten der Schwarzen Nieswurz, in *Berliner Allgemeine Gartenzeitung* No. 11–22, 1858.

Mathew, B.: Alpines '81, Conference Report of the Alpine Garden Society: Hellebores. *Bulletin of the Alpine Garden Society*, 1982.

Mathew, B.: A Survey of Hellebores, in *The Plantsman* 3, 1: 1–10, 1981.

Mathew, B.: *A Gardener's Guide to Hellebores*. Alpine Garden Society, no date.

Mathew, B.: *Hellebores*. Alpine Garden Society, 1989.

Mathew, B. and Grey-Wilson, C.: *Flowers of Yugoslavia*, in *Bulletin of the Alpine Garden Society* 164/165, 1971.

Schiffner, V.: Monographia Hellebororum, in *Nova Acta der Kaiserlich Leop. Carol. Deutschen Akademie der Naturforscher*, Vol. LVI, No. 1. Halle, 1891.

Smith, E.: *Helleborus niger* Hybrids, in *Bulletin of the Hardy Plant Society*, 1970.

Smith, G.: *Flower Arranging in House and Garden*. Pelham Books, London, 1977.

Stahl, M. and Umgelter, H.: *Pflanzenschutz im Zierpflanzenbau*. Verlag Eugen Ulmer, Stuttgart, 1976.

Ulbrich, E.: Die Arten der Gattung *Helleborus* (Tourn.) L. *Blätter zur Staudenkunde*, Berlin-Dahlem, 1938.

HELLEBORE NURSERIES

Marlene Ahlburg, Hohes Feld 22, 3171 Rötgesbüttel, Germany

Helen Ballard, Old Country, Mathon, Malvern, Worcs WR13 5PS, UK

Blackthorn Nursery (A.R. & S.B. White), Kilmeston, Alresford, Hants SO24 0NL, UK

Beth Chatto, White Barn House, Elmstead Market, Colchester, CO7 7DB, UK

Günther Jürgl, 5039 Sürth bei Köln, Germany

Heinz Klose, Staudenkulturen, Rosenstr. 10, 3503 Kassel-Lohfelden, Germany

Will McLewin, Phedar Nursery, Bunkers Hill, Romiley, Stockport SK6 3DS, UK

Roger Poulett, Nurse's Cottage, North Mundham, Chichester, Sussex PO20 6JY, UK

Dr. Hans and Helga Simon, Staudengärtnerei, Staudenweg, 8772 Marktheidenfeld, Germany

Washfield Nursery (Elizabeth Strangman), Horns Road, Hawkhurst, Kent TN18 4QU, UK

GLOSSARY OF BOTANICAL TERMS

acaulescent: without a stem (with radical leaves and flower stems).

acuminate: sharply pointed.

adventitious roots: not growing from the main root but from other parts of the plant e.g. the rhizome.

allotetraploid: a plant with two sets of chromosomes inherited from each of different parents i.e. four sets in all.

anther: pollen-bearing part of the flower.

anthocyanin: cell-sap pigments, blue or red, which produce a number of different hues in the tepals.

bract: protective leaf, cauline leaf, in the area of the inflorescence, differing from true leaves by being more or less greatly reduced.

carpel: seed pod, developed from the ovary. In the case of *Helleborus*, each ovary develops into only a single seed pod or capsule.

caulescent: with a stem bearing both leaves and flowers.

cauline leaf: a bract reduced from, and still resembling, a small leaf, growing on the flower stem.

chlorophyll: green pigment in leaves.

chromosomes: carriers of inherited characters found in every cell in a species in a determined number.

clone: all individuals that are the result of division or other asexual methods of increase of one plant or species are part of a clone. Clones cannot be propagated by seed.

cotyledon: seed leaf, the first to be produced (two, in hellebores), different from the true leaves.

cytology: knowledge of cells.

diploid: species with two sets of chromosomes in each cell, the opposite of a germ-cell, which has only one set.

dominant: an inherited character visible in the appearance of the plant that is able to suppress a parallel inherited character, e.g. the dark flower colour of *Helleborus* 'Torquatus' is retained in the flowers of the F_1 even when the other parent has white flowers.

elaiosome: a whitish body attached to seed, e.g. of *Helleborus niger*, attractive to ants who often carry off the seeds for this reason.

emarginate: notched at the tip.

F_1 generation: first generation produced from two different parents.

F₂ generation: hybrid from a cross between two members of the F_1.

filament: tiny stem bearing the anther.

flavone and flavonol: chemical substances that produce a cream or pale yellow flower. Present in almost all white flowers.

glabrous: hairless.

hilum: the scar on a seed where it was attached to its stalk.

hypocotyl: the short 'stem' between the cotyledons and the primary root.

inflorescence: the part of the shoots on which the flowers are borne, the flower-head.

initial bud: the basal bud, which does not contain the expected number of flowers but only a single part of the future inflorescence from which the rest are successively developed.

internode: part of the stem between two leaf bases.

lobe: a partial division of compound leaves.

meiosis: cell division for the formation of female or male germ cells. The pairs of chromosomes become separated and consequently the number of chromosomes is halved.

morphology: the form and structure of living organisms.

nectary: glandular organ of the flower, secretes nectar.

ovary: fruiting body, holds the female germ-cells or ovules.

palmate: leaf form resembling a hand.

pedate: literally foot-shaped. In the case of the hellebore leaf, a curved comb- or rake-shape might be a better description.

pedicel: short stem bearing a single flower.

perianth: corona, made up of sepals or petals or both together.

petiole: stem of a leaf, bract or nectary.

phenotype: the whole of the visible characteristics determined by the genes of the individual plant.

photosynthesis: storing of the sun's energy in the form of sugar and starch through the action of chlorophyll.

placenta: tissue in the ovary by which the female germ-cell is attached.

plumule: bud between the two cotyledons from which all further parts of the plant develop.

protogyny: the ripening of the female germ-cells and reproductive organs before those of the male germ-cells (pollen) on the same plant.

raphe: longish strip of tissue, a narrow roll.

receptacle: the enlarged upper end of the stem bearing the flower.

recessive: a character that is not visible, a suppressed inheritance.

rhizome: underground, usually horizontally developed, branched shoot; roots grow from the underside, the above-ground parts of the plant from the terminal bud. Also known as the rootstock.

self-fertile: the pollen of a plant can fertilize the female germ-cells of the same plant.

sepals: parts of the corona; circle of flower parts below the petals.

tepals: sepals and petals, mostly used in cases where it is difficult to decide which they are, as in hellebores.

terminal bud: bud at the upper end of the rootstock or stem.

tetraploid: a plant with four sets of chromosomes in each cell.

tissue culture, *in vitro* culture: laboratory techniques used to propagate plants from tiny pieces of different kinds of tissue of the original plant.

INDEX

Page numbers in *italic* indicate line drawings; numbers in **bold** refer to colour plates

acaulescent 19, 122
Acaulescentes 10, 11, 18, 19, 21, *22*, 26, 27, *27*, 28, 29, *30*, 32, 35, 36–57, 94
adaptation to climate 8, 9, 92, 101, 102
adventitious roots *16*, 18, 19, *20*, 122
aggregate bud 22, 24, 31
allotetraploid 84, 122
anthers 11, 26, 33, 74, 122
anthocyanin 89, 122
aphides 105
Archer-Hind, T. 72, 83
artificial light 56, 59

Balearic Hellebore see *H. lividus*
Ballard, H. 7, **8**, 71, 77, 84–6, 88, 90–1, 120
    named cultivars **6**, **7**, 85–6, 88
basal sheaths 19, 21, *21*
Bladder Hellebore see *H. vesicarius*
blade 21, 24, 26, 28, 29, *29*, 31
Bowles, E.A. 38
bracts 10, 21, 22, *22*, *23*, 24, *25*, 26, 29–31, *29*, *30*, *32*, 122
branching 22, *22*, 24, *25*, 26
Braun, A. 83, 90

capsules 9, 10, 34, *67*
carpels *32*, *34*, 35, *66*, 75, 94, 95, 122
caulescent 19, 122
Caulescentes 9, 10, 11, 18, 19, 21, 22, 24, 26, 27, 28, 29, 31, 32, 58–68, 84, 94, 98, 103–4, 108, 110–12
cauline leaves *22*, 26, *27*, 29, *30*, 31, 122
Chinese Hellebore see *H. thibetanus*
chlorophyll 31, 122
Christmas Rose see *H. niger*
chromosomes 69, 122
classification 37, 84, 86–7
climatic variation 92
companion plants 107–14
Coniothyrium 106
Corsican Hellebore see *H. argutifolius*
cotyledons 15, *17*, 96, 122
    tube 15, *17*
crêpe- (wrinkled) skin 10, 32, 82

crown 19, 27
cultivation 26, 92–104
cytology 84, 122

Dark Red Hellebore see *H. atrorubens*
deciduous species 9, 10, 27
diseases 105–6
dispersion 8
distribution 12–14
division
    of leaflets 26–7
    of plants 19, 93–4
dominant 88–9, 122
dormant bud 21, *22*
double-flowered forms **7**, 72, 86
early-flowering forms 39, 56, 73–4, 79, 98, 103, 108
eelworm 105
elaiosome 95, 122
embryo 35
endosperm 35
evergreen species 9, 27, 79
evolution 8–11, 87

False Honeydew 106
fertility 11, 73, 74
fertilizer 99, 100, 106
filaments 11, 33, 123
Fish, M. 69, 86
flavones 89, 123
floristry 115–16
flower
    arranging 116–17
    bud 22, *22*, 24, 31
    colour 33, 88–91, 109
    structure *32*
flowering size 18, 96
follicles 34
forcing 115–16
fragrance 10–11, 33, 41, 42
Fragrant Hellebore see *H. odorus*
Fröbel, O. 83
fruit 34, *34*
Fuchs, H. & J. 7, 43, 44, 112

fungicide 105–6
fungus diseases 77, 103, 105–6

genetics 84, 88–9, 103
germination 94–5, 96–7
Grecian (Greek) Hellebore see *H. cyclophyllus*
greenfly 105
Green Hellebore see *H. viridis*

hardiness 8, 95–6, 101–4
Hedge Hellebore see *H. dumetorum*
Hegi, G. 84, 120
Heinemann nursery 83
hellebore nurseries 121
Helleborin 119
Helleborus
  antiquorum (*H. orientalis*) 37, 39
  argutifolius **5**, 10, *13*, 14, *16*, 18, *18, 19*, 21, 22, *23*, 24, *27, 29*, 31, 33, 35, 61, 62–3, *63*, 76, 78, 96, 102, 104, 110, 111, 116–17
  argutifolius × *H. foetidus* 10, 84
  atrorubens **3**, *13*, 51, *51*, 69, 70, 113
  bocconei see *H. multifidus* subsp. *bocconei*
  caucasicus (*H. orientalis*) 37, 38
  chinensis see *H. thibetanus*
  corsicus see *H. argutifolius*
  cyclophyllus **3**, 9, 10, 11, 12, *13*, 32, 33, 34, 39, 41, *41*, 42, 46, 93–4, 112, 113
  dumetorum 10, 12, *13*, 27, *30*, 33, 50, *50*, 51, 53, 69, 71, 108, 113
  foetidus **5**, 10, 11, *13*, 14, *16*, 18, *18, 20*, 21, 22, 24, *25, 27, 29*, 31, 32, 34, 35, 64–5, *64, 65*, 96, 101, 102, 110, 111, 116, 118
    'Wester Flisk' 111
  'Intermedius' 12, *13*, 69–71, *70*, 114
  kochii (*H. orientalis*) 32, 38, 83, 90
  lividus **5**, 10, *13*, 14, 18, 21, 22, *22*, 24, 26, 27, *27, 29*, 31, 33, 34, *34*, 58–61, *59*, 76, 77, 78, 96, 102, 108, 112, 116, 117
    'Pictus' 59–61, 78
  multifidus 11, 12, *13*, 27, *30*, 33, 43–7, *43*, 53, 70, 91, 105, 112–13, 116–17
    subsp. *bocconei* 12, *13*, 33, 41, 44, *45*, 112
      (*H. siculus*) **3**, *22*, 26, 27, *30*, 41, 44–7, *45*, 108
    subsp. *hercegovinus* **3**, 43, 112
    subsp. *istriacus* 43
    subsp. *serbicus* see *H. torquatus*
  niger 9, 10, 11, *13*, 14, 18, *20*, 26, 27, *27*, 29, 31, 32, 33, 34, 35, 39, 54–7, 61, 73, 76, 77, 80, 84, 93, 96, 98, 99, 101–2, 105, 106, 111, 115–16, 117, 118, 119
    subsp. *macranthus* **4**, 10, 32, 54–6, *55*, 88, 108, 111
    subsp. *niger* **4**, 54–6
      'Praecox' 40, 54, *54*, 56, 73, 93, 98, 106, 108, 111, 115–16
    × *H. lividus* 61, 77, *77*
  × *nigercors* **6**, 61, 73, *73, 74*, 76, 77, 94, 101, 111
    'Alabaster' 76, 85
  × *nigristern* 76
  odorus **4**, 9, 10, 12, *13, 16*, 21, 27, 33, 41, 42, *42*, 43, 53, 112, 113
    subsp. *laxus* 42, 88
  olympicus (*H. orientalis*) 37, *37*, 39, 83, 88
  orientalis **1**, **2**, **3**, 9, 10, 12, *13, 21*, 27, 32, 33, 34, 37–40, *37*, 41, 83, 88, 108, 118
    subsp. *abchasicus* *13, 16, 18*, 37, 39–40, *39*, 83
    subsp. *guttatus* **2**, *13*, 33, 37, 40, 83, 90, 105, 116
  ponticus (*H. orientalis*) 38
  purpurascens **3**, 10, 12, *13*, 27, 32, 48, 49, *49*, 90, 112, 114
  × *sternii* 61, 78, 101, 110–11, 117
    'Wintersilber' **8**, 78, 79, *79*, 94, 101, 111
  thibetanus 9, 12, 14, 15, 36
  torquatus 12, *13, 25*, 48, *48*, 69, 72, 90, 112
    'Torquatus' **6**, 12, 48, 69, 70, 71, 72, *72*, 91, 113–14
  vesicarius 9, 10, 11, 12, *13*, 15, *17*, 28, 31, 32, 34, 35, 66–8, *66, 67*, 97
  viridis **4**, 10, 12, 14, 50, 52–3, 112, 118, 119
    subsp. *occidentalis* *13*, 52–3, *53*
    subsp. *viridis* *13*, 52–3, *52*
Helleborus cultivars
  'Aeneas' 72, 85, 86
  'Atropurpureus' 28
  'Atrorubens' ('Early Purple') 26, *30*, 33, 39, 73, 80–2, *81*, 90, 96, 98, 108, 112, 116
  'Black Knight' **7**, 83
  'Blowsy' 85
  'Blue Spray' 85
  'Blue Wisp' **7**, 85
  'Bowles' Yellow' 38–9
  'Brunhilde' 88
  'Button' 85
  'Cheerful' 85
  'Citron' 85, *85*, 88
  'Cosmos' 85
  'Dawn' 85
  'Dick Crandon' 85
  'Dido' 72, 85, 86
  'Dotty' 85
  'Dusk' 85

'Early Purple' see 'Atrorubens'
'Elizabeth Strangman's Pink' **6**
'Frühlingsfreude' 88
'Frühlingsrose' **1**
'Frühlingsschale' 86
'Galathé' **6**, 73, 98, 108
'Garnet' 85
'Gewitternacht' 86
'Greencups' **6**, 85
'Hades' 85
'Hecate' 85
'Helen Ballard' 85
'Hercules' 85
'Indigo' 85
'Ingot' 85
'Lynne' 85
'Monika' 90
'Nachthimmel' 86
'Nocturne' 85
'Parrot' 85
'Patchwork' 85–6
'Philip Ballard' 85
'Philip Wilson' 85
'Picoté' 80
'Primrose Dame' 83
'Rembrandt' 86
'Rosa' 86
'Rossini' 86
'Rubens' 85
'Schwarzes Gold' 86
'Scorpio' 85
'Sirius' 85
'Sunny' 86
'Sylvia' **7**, 85
'Upstart' 85
'Ushba' **6**, 85, 93
'Zodiac Strain' **2**, 85
Hellebrin 119
hilum 35, 123
hybridization 10, 11, 69, 73–5, 88–91
hybrids **1**, **2**, **7**, **8**, *44*, 69, 83–6, *91*
hypocotyl 15, *16*, 19, 123

inflorescence 19, 22–6, *22, 23, 25*, 29, 31, 123
Ingwersen 72
initial bud 22, 31, 123
internode 123

Jürgl, G. 86

keel 33, 35
Klose, H. 7, 86, 88, 90
    named cultivars 86, 88, 90
Koch, K. 83, 120

labelling 75, 96
leaf forms 26, *27, 37, 39, 41, 42, 43, 44, 45, 48, 49, 50, 51, 52, 53, 54, 55, 59, 63, 64, 65, 70, 72, 73, 77, 79, 81, 85, 91*
leaflets 15, *16*, 18, 22, 26–7
leaf scars *20*, 21
leaves 15, 18, 21, *23*, 26–8, 31, 91, 101–4, 109, 110, 112–13, 116
    use in identification 26, *39*
Leichtlin, M. 83, 90
Lenten Hellebore see *H. orientalis*
Lenten Roses **2**, 73, 86, 93, 96, 98, 99, 102–3, 107, 108, 109, 116
lime 93–4, 99, 100, 105
liquid manure 100
lobes 29, 43, 123

Mathew, B. 7, 12, 15, 44, 67, 69, 84, 86–7, 120
medicine 118–19
membranous bracts 22, 24, 26, *29*, 31, 54, 64
morphology 9, 11, 15–35, 123
Much-Divided Hellebore see *H. multifidus*
mulch 99, 101, 104

natural hybrids 69
naturalizing 96, 107
nectar 10, 11
nectaries 10, 11, 32, *32*, 34, *66*, 91, 123
nematodes 105, 106

Oriental Hellebore see *H. orientalis*
Orientalis Group see Lenten Roses
ovary 9, 10, 26, 33, 34, 69, 123

palmate leaf 26, 27, *27*, 123
pedate leaf 26, 27, *27*, 123
pedicels 10, 22, 31, 106, 123
Peronospora pulveracea 106
pests 105
petals 10, 32
petioles 19, 21, 24, 26, 29, *29*, 32, 106, 123
photosynthesis 22, 29, 31, 123
pistil *66*
planting 98–99
    sites 99–100, 107–14
plumule 15, 123
pod parent 74, 96
poisoning 118–19
pollen 11, 69, 74
    parent 74
pollination 10, 11, 32, 34, 74, 75
pot plants 79, 116
preserving leaves 116
propagation 93–7
Protoanemonin 119

protogyny 11, 74, 123
Purple Hellebore see *H. purpurascens*

radical-leaved species see Acaulescentes
radical leaves 21, *22*, 27, *27*, 28
raphe 35, 123
receptacle 9, *32*, 33, 34, 123
recessive 88, 89, 123
Red Christmas Rose see *H.* 'Atrorubens'
reduced leaves 24, 28, 29, *30*, 31
Rhizoctonia solani 106
Rhizoma Hellebori 119
rhizome *16*, 18, 19, *19*, *20*, 21, *21*, 27, 123
roots 15, *16*, *17*, 18, 19, *20*, 95, 96, 98, 99

sacs 33
scales 21, 24, 28
scent see fragrance
Schiffner, V. 7, 12, *16*, *18*, 44, 46, 50, 53, 59,
    66, 69, 83, 84, 116, 120
Schleicher, Prof. 83
seed *16*, 24, 34, 35, *66*, 75, 94–7
    dormancy 94–5, 97
    sowing 95
seedlings 15–18, *16*, *17*, *18*, 94–7
selected forms 38–9, 71
sepals 32, 124
Serbian Hellebore see *H. torquatus*
sheaths 19, *21*, *23*, 28, 31
shoot bud *16*, 19, *19*, *20*, 21
shoots *20*, 101
side bud 19
Smith, E. 76, 85, 88, 120
    named cultivars 85

snails 105
Snow Rose see *H. niger*
soils 98–9
species descriptions 36–68
stamens *32*, 34, *66*
stem 19, *20*, 21, 22, *22*, *23*, 24, *25*, 26, 27, 28,
    29, 31, *34*, *66*, *67*, 74, 101–4, 110, 116,
    117
stemmed species see Caulescentes
Stern, Sir Frederick 61, 83
stigma 33, 74
Stinking Hellebore see *H. foetidus*
Strangman, E. 72, 76, 85
styles 33, 34, *66*, 74, 75
summergreen species 27, 36
supplementary buds 26

tepals 10, 24, *32*, *34*, *66*, 74, 124
terminal bud 19, *20*, 21, 27, 28, 45, 124
tetraploid 89, 124
tissue culture 93, 124
trace elements 93, 99, 100, 105
transitional elements 10
    forms 32, 37
    leaves 31, 32
transplanting 98–9

Ulbrich, E. 7, 9, 12, *13*, 36, 58, 69, 84,
    120

veins 26, *30*
virus diseases 106

wintergreen species 28
winter treatment 101–4